Macmillan/McGraw-Hill • Glencoe

Math Triumphs

Grade 4

Book 1: Number and Operations and Algebra

Authors

Basich Whitney • Brown • Dawson • Gonsalves • Silbey • Vielhaber

D1265355

**Macmillan/McGraw-Hill
Glencoe**

Photo Credits

All coins photographed by United States Mint.
All bills photographed by Michael Houghton/StudiOhio.
Cover, i BananaStock/Jupiter Images; **iv** (tl)File Photo, (tc tr)The McGraw-Hill Companies, (cl c)Doug Martin, (cr)Aaron Haupt, (bl bc)File Photo; **v** (L to R 1 2 3 4 6 7 8 9 11 12) The McGraw-Hill Companies, (5 10 13 14)File Photo; **vi** Digital Vision/PunchStock; **vii** PictureNet/CORBIS; **viii** Masterfile; **1** Goodshoot/Fotosearch; **2** Sandro Vannini/CORBIS; **27** Jupiter Images; **52** Marnie Burkhart/Masterfile; **60** CORBIS/Punchstock; **64** David Buffington/CORBIS; **66** Masterfile; **68** Photodisc/Getty Images; **80** Richard Ransier/CORBIS; **88** Photodisc/Getty Images; **93** Mint Girl Productions/Getty Images; **96** Barbara Peacock/Getty Images; **104** Ryan McVay/Getty Images; **110** Digital Vision/SuperStock; **116** Dynamic Graphics Value/SuperStock; **124** Lawrence Manning/CORBIS; **129** Siede Preis/Getty Images; **130** Lawrence Manning/CORBIS; **137** Photodisc/Getty Images; **140** Mike Greenlar/Syracuse Newspapers/The Image Works; **145** Dynamic Graphics Group/PunchStock; **150** (t)C Squared Studios/Getty Images, (b)Stockdisc/PunchStock; **157** (t)C Squared Studios/Getty Images, (b)GK Hart/Vikki Hart/Getty Images; **158** Creatas/PunchStock; **165** Comstock/Jupiter Images; **171** Peter Finger/CORBIS

The McGraw-Hill Companies

 Macmillan/McGraw-Hill
Glencoe

Copyright © 2009 by The McGraw-Hill Companies, Inc. All rights reserved. Except as permitted under the United States Copyright Act, no part of this publication may be reproduced or distributed in any form or by any means, or stored in a database or retrieval system, without prior permission of the publisher.

Send all inquiries to:
Glencoe/McGraw-Hill
8787 Orion Place
Columbus, OH 43240-4027

ISBN: 978-0-07-888201-2
MHID: 0-07-888201-X

Math Triumphs
Grade 4, Book 1

Printed in the United States of America.

6 7 8 9 10 HSO 16 15 14 13 12 11 10

Math Triumphs

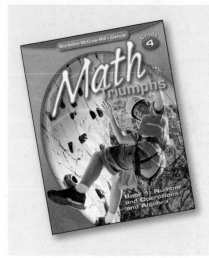

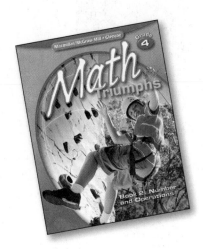

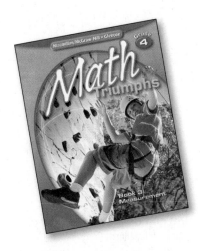

Copyright © Glencoe/McGraw-Hill, a division of The McGraw-Hill Companies, Inc.

Authors and Consultants

AUTHORS

Frances Basich Whitney
Project Director, Mathematics K–12
Santa Cruz County Office of Education
Capitola, California

Kathleen M. Brown
Math Curriculum Staff Developer
Washington Middle School
Long Beach, California

Dixie Dawson
Math Curriculum Leader
Long Beach Unified
Long Beach, California

Philip Gonsalves
Mathematics Coordinator
Alameda County Office of Education
Hayward, California

Robyn Silbey
Math Specialist
Montgomery County Public Schools
Gaithersburg, Maryland

Kathy Vielhaber
Mathematics Consultant
St. Louis, Missouri

CONTRIBUTING AUTHORS

Viken Hovsepian
Professor of Mathematics
Rio Hondo College
Whittier, California

FOLDABLES Study Organizer **Dinah Zike**
Educational Consultant
Dinah-Might Activities, Inc.
San Antonio, Texas

CONSULTANTS

Assessment

Donna M. Kopenski, Ed.D.
Math Coordinator K–5
City Heights Educational Collaborative
San Diego, California

Instructional Planning and Support

Beatrice Luchin
Mathematics Consultant
League City, Texas

ELL Support and Vocabulary

ReLeah Cossett Lent
Author/Educational Consultant
Alford, Florida

Copyright © Glencoe/McGraw-Hill, a division of The McGraw-Hill Companies, Inc.

Reviewers

Each person below reviewed at least two chapters of the Student Study Guide, providing feedback and suggestions for improving the effectiveness of the mathematics instruction.

Dana M. Addis
Teacher Leader
Dearborn Public Schools
Dearborn, MI

Renee M. Blanchard
Elementary Math Facilitator
Erie School District
Erie, PA

Jeanette Collins Cantrell
5th and 6th Grade Math Teacher
W.R. Castle Memorial Elementary
Wittensville, KY

Helen L. Cheek
K-5 Mathematics Specialist
Durham Public Schools
Durham, NC

Mercy Cosper
1st Grade Teacher
Pershing Park Elementary
Killeen, TX

Bonnie H. Ennis
Mathematics Coordinator
Wicomico County Public Schools
Salisbury, MD

Sheila A. Evans
Instructional Support Teacher—Math
Glenmount Elementary/Middle School
Baltimore, MD

Lisa B. Golub
Curriculum Resource Teacher
Millennia Elementary
Orlando, FL

Donna Hagan
Program Specialist—Special Programs
   Department
Weatherford ISD
Weatherford, TX

Russell Hinson
Teacher
Belleview Elementary
Rock Hill, SC

Tania Shepherd Holbrook
Teacher
Central Elementary School
Paintsville, KY

Stephanie J. Howard
3rd Grade Teacher
Preston Smith Elementary
Lubbock, TX

Rhonda T. Inskeep
Math Support Teacher
Stevens Forest Elementary School
Columbia, MD

Albert Gregory Knights
Teacher/4th Grade/Math Lead Teacher
Cornelius Elementary
Houston, TX

Barbara Langley
Math/Science Coach
Poinciana Elementary School
Kissimmee, FL

David Ennis McBroom
Math/Science Facilitator
John Motley Morehead Elementary
Charlotte, NC

Jan Mercer, MA; NBCT
K-5 Math Lab Facilitator
Meadow Woods Elementary
Orlando, FL

Rosalind R. Mohamed
Instructional Support Teacher—Mathematics
Furley Elementary School
Baltimore, MD

Patricia Penafiel
Teacher
Phyllis Miller Elementary
Miami, FL

Lindsey R. Petlak
2nd Grade Instructor
Prairieview Elementary School
Hainesville, IL

Lana A. Prichard
District Math Resource Teacher K-8
Lawrence Co. School District
Louisa, KY

Stacy L. Riggle
3rd Grade Spanish Magnet Teacher
Phillips Elementary
Pittsburgh, PA

Wendy Scheleur
5th Grade Teacher
Piney Orchard Elementary
Odenton, MD

Stacey L. Shapiro
Teacher
Zilker Elementary
Austin, TX

Kim Wilkerson Smith
4th Grade Teacher
Casey Elementary School
Austin, TX

Wyolonda M. Smith, NBCT
4th Grade Teacher
Pilot Elementary School
Greensboro, NC

Kristen M. Stone
3rd Grade Teacher
Tanglewood Elementary
Lumberton, NC

Jamie M. Williams
Math Specialist
New York Mills Union Free School District
New York Mills, NY

Copyright © Glencoe/McGraw-Hill, a division of The McGraw-Hill Companies, Inc.

Contents

Chapter 1 — Place Value and Patterns

Pulliam Peak, Jefferson, Texas

Copyright © Glencoe/McGraw-Hill, a division of The McGraw-Hill Companies, Inc.

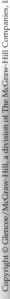

Chapter 2 **Multiplication**

Gateway Arch, St. Louis, Missouri

Copyright © Glencoe/McGraw-Hill, a division of The McGraw-Hill Companies, Inc.

Contents

Chapter 3

More Multiplication

Miami Beach, Florida

Copyright © Glencoe/McGraw-Hill, a division of The McGraw-Hill Companies, Inc.

Chapter 4

Introduction to Division

Brooklyn Bridge, New York, New York

Copyright © Glencoe/McGraw-Hill, a division of The McGraw-Hill Companies, Inc.

Place Value and Patterns

How many bees do you see?

Suppose you were to count a large population of bees, animals, or even people. You could use place value. Place value helps you to understand how great or small an amount is. Look at the bees. How many bees do you think are there?

STEP 1 Quiz

Are you ready for Chapter 1? Take the Online Readiness Quiz at *macmillanmh.com* to find out.

STEP 2 Preview

Get ready for Chapter 1. Review these skills and compare them with what you will learn in this chapter.

What You Know	What You Will Learn
You know that 2 ten-dollar bills and 4 one-dollar bills equal $24. Dollar amounts can be written in different ways.	*Lessons 1-1, 1-2, 1-4* Numbers like 4,524 can be written in different ways. **word form:** four thousand, five hundred twenty-four **expanded form:** 4,000 + 500 + 20 + 4
You know how to locate numbers on a number line. 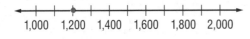 1,000 1,200 1,400 1,600 1,800 2,000	*Lesson 1-3* You can use a number line to compare numbers. 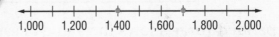 1,000 1,200 1,400 1,600 1,800 2,000 1,400 is **less than** 1,700
You know how to use addition patterns. Your backpack can hold 4 textbooks. If your friend has a backpack just like yours, how many textbooks could you both carry in your backpacks? _____ Add 4 textbooks for each additional backpack. 	*Lesson 1-5 and 1-6* **Patterns** follow rules. The rule is "each backpack can hold 4 textbooks." 1 backpack ⇒ 4 textbooks 2 backpacks ⇒ 8 textbooks 3 backpacks ⇒ 12 textbooks 4 backpacks ⇒ 16 textbooks Add 4 textbooks for each backpack.

Whole Numbers to 1,000

KEY Concept

Standard form is the way to write a number using **digits**.

Place value is the value assigned to each digit in a number based on its position in the number.

125

hundreds	tens	ones
1	2	5
1 × 100	2 × 10	5 × 1
100	20	5

Expanded form shows the value of each digit added together.

$$100 + 20 + 5$$

Word form is the way to say, read, or write a number.

Say:

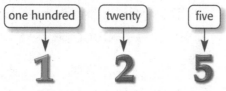

one hundred → **1** twenty → **2** five → **5**

Write: one hundred twenty-five

You can also write 125 in short word form:
1 hundred, 2 tens, 5 ones.

Copyright © by The McGraw-Hill Companies, Inc.

VOCABULARY

digit
the numbers 0, 1, 2, 3, 4, 5, 6, 7, 8, and 9

expanded form
writing a number as a sum that shows the value of each digit

place value
the value given to a digit by its position in a number

standard form
writing a number using only digits

word form
writing numbers using only words

A number can have a zero in any place. The number 305 has 3 hundreds, 0 tens, and 5 ones. The expanded form is 300 + 5.

Example 1

Write five hundred forty-two in standard form.

1. There are 5 hundreds in the number.

2. There are 4 tens in the number.

3. There are 2 ones in the number.

4. Write each digit in the correct place in the place-value chart.

100	10	1
hundreds	tens	ones
5	4	2

The number in standard form is 542.

YOUR TURN!

Write three hundred ninety-three in standard form.

1. How many hundreds are in the number? _____

2. How many tens are in the number?

   _____

3. How many ones are in the number?

   _____

100	10	1
hundreds	tens	ones

4. Write each digit in the correct place in the place-value chart.

The number in standard form is _____.

Example 2

Write 803 in both word form and expanded form.

1. Write the words as you read or say the number.
   eight hundred three

   > Note there is a zero in the tens place value.

2. Look at each digit. Write the short word form of the number.
   8 hundreds, 3 ones

3. Write the expanded form of the number. Use the short word form to help. **800 + 3**

YOUR TURN!

Write 756 in both word form and expanded form.

1. Write the words as you read the number.

   _____

2. Look at each digit. Write the short word form of the number.

   _____

3. Write the expanded form of the number. Use the short word form to help.

   _____

Copyright © by The McGraw-Hill Companies, Inc.

GO ON

Who is Correct?

Write 900 + 10 + 9 in standard form.

Kathy
9,109

Ashton
911

Malina
919

Circle correct answer(s). Cross out incorrect answer(s).

 Guided Practice

Identify the form of the number shown.

1 400 + 20 + 7 _____

2 376 _____

Step by Step Practice

3 **Write three hundred seventy-five in standard form.**

Step 1 How many hundreds are in the number? _____

Step 2 How many tens are in the number? _____

Step 3 How many ones are in the number? _____

Step 4 Write each digit in the correct place in the place-value chart.

Step 5 The number in standard form is _____.

100	10	1
hundreds	tens	ones

Write each number in standard form.

4 seven hundred eighty-two _____

5 three hundred six _____

Write each number in expanded form.

6 315 _____

7 507 _____

8 Write 235 in both word forms. _____

Copyright © by The McGraw-Hill Companies, Inc.

Step by Step *Problem-Solving Practice*

Problem-Solving Strategies
- ☑ Draw a diagram.
- ☐ Use logical reasoning.
- ☐ Solve a simpler problem.
- ☐ Work backward.
- ☐ Guess and check.

9 **PUZZLES**   Use the digits 3, 4, and 5 to make the greatest number. Use each digit once.

Understand   Read the problem. Write what you know.

You can use _____, _____, and _____.

Plan   Pick a strategy. One strategy is to draw a diagram. Create a place-value chart.

Solve   Which digit gives you the greatest value in the hundreds place? _____

Which of the two remaining digits gives you the greater value in the tens place? _____

What digit do you put in the ones place? _____

The greatest number you can make is _____.

100	10	1
hundreds	tens	ones

Check   Write all the other possible numbers you can make. Check them on a number line.

10 **PUZZLES**   Use the digits 9, 6, and 3 to make the least possible number. Use each digit once. Check off each step.

_____ **Understand: I circled key words.**

_____ **Plan: To solve the problem, I will** _____.

_____ **Solve: The answer is** _____.

_____ **Check: I checked my answer by** _____.

11 **Reflect**   Write a rule to solve problems like 9 and 10 above (creating the greatest or least number from three digits).

_____

_____

_____

Copyright © by The McGraw-Hill Companies, Inc.

GO ON

Skills, Concepts, and Problem Solving

Write each number in standard form.

12 six hundred twenty-two _____

13 3 hundreds, 3 ones _____

Write each number in both word forms.

14 135 _____

15 633 _____

Write each number in expanded form.

16 412 _____

17 707 _____

Write the missing number in the equation.

18 $800 + \text{\_\_\_\_} + 2 = 832$

19 $500 + 30 + \text{\_\_\_\_} = 539$

Solve.

20 PUZZLES   Use the digits 1, 2, and 3 to make the least number possible. Use each digit only once. _____

21 CELL PHONE   Casey has 115 phone numbers saved in her cell phone. How many sets of hundreds, tens, and ones are there in 115? _____

Vocabulary Check   **Write the vocabulary word that completes each sentence.**

22 A number written as an expression that shows the values of the digits is in _____.

23 The place value of the first digit on the left in a three-digit number is _____.

24 Writing in Math   Explain the different methods to represent a three-digit number. Show examples.

_____

_____

STOP

Copyright © by The McGraw-Hill Companies, Inc.

Whole Numbers Less Than 10,000

KEY Concept

Place value tells you the value of each digit in a number.

1,234

	thousands	hundreds	tens	ones
Standard Form	1	2	3	4
Model				

1,234 in expanded form is

$$1,000 + 200 + 30 + 4$$

VOCABULARY

expanded form
the form of a number as a sum that shows the value of each digit

place value
the value given to a digit by its position in a number

standard form
writing a number using only digits

The **expanded form** of a number shows the value of each digit. It uses the operation of addition.

Example 1

Identify the value of the underlined digit in 3,4̲85.

1. Write the number in a place-value chart.

2. The underlined digit is in the hundreds place.

3. Replace all the digits to the right of the underlined digit with zeros.

4. The underlined digit has a value of 400.

1000	100	10	1
thousands	hundreds	tens	ones
3	4̲	8	5

Copyright © by The McGraw-Hill Companies, Inc.

GO ON

YOUR TURN!

Identify the value of the underlined digit in 7,8<u>9</u>5.

1. Write the number in the place-value chart.

2. In what place is the underlined digit?_____

3. Replace all the digits to the right of the underlined digit with zeros.

4. What is the value of the underlined digit? _____

1000	100	10	1
thousands	hundreds	tens	ones

Example 2

Write 5,638 in expanded form.

1. Write the number in a place-value chart.

1000	100	10	1
thousands	hundreds	tens	ones
5	6	3	8

2. Write the value of each digit shown in the place-value chart.

5 → 5 × 1,000 = 5,000
6 → 6 × 100 = 600
3 → 3 × 10 = 30
8 → 8 × 1   = 8

3. Write the expanded form of 5,638.
5000 + 600 + 30 + 8

YOUR TURN!

Write 9,607 in expanded form.

1. Write the number in a place-value chart.

1000	100	10	1
thousands	hundreds	tens	ones

2. Write the value of each digit shown in the place-value chart.

_____

_____

_____

_____

3. Write the expanded form of 9,607.

_____

Who is Correct?

What is the value of the underlined digit in <u>2</u>,075?

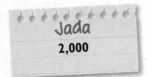
Jada
2,000

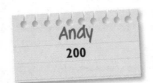
Andy
200

Victor
20

Circle correct answer(s). Cross out incorrect answer(s).

Copyright © by The McGraw-Hill Companies, Inc.

▶ Guided Practice

Identify the digit in the thousands place-value position of each number.

1 1,414 _____

2 3,007 _____

Step by Step Practice

3 Identify the value of the underlined digit in 8,230.

Step 1 Write the number in a place-value chart.

Step 2 The place value of the 8 is _____.

Step 3 Add _____ zeros to the right of the digit.

Step 4 The underlined digit has a value of _____.

1000	100	10	1
thousands	hundreds	tens	ones

Identify the value of each underlined digit.

4 2,1<u>6</u>9

1000	100	10	1
thousands	hundreds	tens	ones

_____

5 7,<u>1</u>05 _____

6 4,<u>7</u>98 _____

7 8<u>7</u>3 _____

8 1<u>6</u>4 _____

9 <u>2</u>,938 _____

10 <u>7</u>,512 _____

Write each number in expanded form.

11 8,232

12 7,159

13 2,309

_____

_____

_____

14 4,715

15 6,400

16 1,738

_____

_____

_____

Write each number in standard form.

17 3,000 + 900 + 70 + 4 _____

18 5,000 + 200 + 30 + 1 _____

19 6,000 + 7 _____

20 8,000 + 8 _____

GO ON

Copyright © by The McGraw-Hill Companies, Inc.

Step by Step Problem-Solving Practice

Problem-Solving Strategies
☐ Act it out.
☑ Draw a diagram.
☐ Work backward.
☐ Solve a simpler problem.
☐ Look for a pattern.

21 **SPORTS** The number on Quinn's baseball uniform has the same value as the tens place in his address. Quinn lives at 1452 Elm Street. What number does Quinn wear on his uniform?

Understand Read the problem. Write what you know.

The number in Quinn's address is _____.

Plan Pick a strategy. One strategy is to draw a diagram. Write the number in a place-value chart.

Solve

1000	100	10	1
thousands	hundreds	tens	ones

The _____ is in the tens place.
Multiply by _____ to find the value.
The number on Quinn's uniform is _____.

Check You can model Quinn's address using base-ten blocks. Count the number of rods.

22 **SCHOOL** Corinna's locker combination uses two-digit numbers. The first number in her combination has the same value as the tens place of her homeroom number. Corinna has homeroom in Room 435. What is the first number in Corinna's locker combination? Check off each step.

_____ Understand: I circled key words.

_____ Plan: To solve the problem, I will _____.

_____ Solve: The answer is _____.

_____ Check: I checked my answer by _____.

23 **PUZZLES** Use the digits 3, 4, 7, and 2 to write the greatest possible number that is even. Use each digit once. _____

24 **PUZZLES** Use the digits 9, 6, 7, and 3 to write the least possible number that is even. Use each digit once. _____

Copyright © by The McGraw-Hill Companies, Inc.

25 **Reflect** Explain how to find the place value of the underlined digit in 7,318.

_____

_____

▶ Skills, Concepts, and Problem Solving

Write _true_ or _false_ for each statement. If a statement is false, change the statement to make it true.

26 The place-value positions of four-digit numbers include ten thousands, hundreds, tens, and ones.

_____

27 In a four-digit number, the number farthest left is the thousands digit.

_____

Write each number in standard form.

28 8,000 + 800 + 2 _____

1000	100	10	1
thousands	hundreds	tens	ones

29 5,000 + 200 + 50 + 2 _____

1000	100	10	1
thousands	hundreds	tens	ones

30 2,000 + 300 + 50 + 1 _____

31 7,000 + 500 _____

32 9,000 + 800 + 7 _____

33 1,000 + 100 + 10 _____

34 6,000 + 60 _____

35 3,000 + 700 + 80 + 9 _____

36 5,000 + 10 _____

37 4,000 + 900 + 7 _____

Write each number in expanded form.

38 5,480 _____

39 2,985 _____

40 5,005 _____

41 8,713 _____

GO ON

Copyright © by The McGraw-Hill Companies, Inc.

Solve.

42 PUZZLES   Use the digits 5, 7, 3, and 4 to write the greatest possible odd number. Use each digit only once. _____

43 PUZZLES   Use the digits 1, 2, 9, and 7 to write the greatest possible even number. Use each digit only once. _____

44 FINANCE   Anand is saving money for a new sound system. He currently has one 100-dollar bill, seven 10-dollar bills, and nine 1-dollar bills. How much money has Anand saved? Use the place-value chart at the right. _____

100	10	1
hundreds	tens	ones

45 FINANCE   Elena's older sister received a handwritten check from a friend. The hundreds digit in the check amount of 1,?40 was erased. The value of the digit was 600. What was the digit? _____

Vocabulary Check   **Write the vocabulary word that completes each sentence.**

46 The value given to a digit by its position is the _____.

47 The _____ place is to the left of the hundreds place.

48 Writing in Math   Explain the difference between standard form and expanded form.

_____

_____

_____

 Spiral Review

Write each number in standard form. (Lesson 1-1, p. 4)

49 three hundred fifty-two _____

50 400 + 60 + 9 _____

51 700 + 3 _____

52 eight hundred seventy _____

STOP

Copyright © by The McGraw-Hill Companies, Inc.

Write each number in standard form and in expanded form.

1 four hundred ten

_____

2 5 hundred, 2 ones

_____

3 one hundred six

_____

4 7 hundreds, 9 tens, 9 ones

_____

5 six thousand nine hundred fifteen   _____

Identify the value of the underlined digit.

6 2,<u>4</u>03 _____

7 1,8<u>2</u>1 _____

8 4,34<u>8</u> _____

9 <u>3</u>,909 _____

10 9,0<u>7</u>0 _____

11 6,<u>8</u>36 _____

12 <u>7</u>,358 _____

13 <u>8</u>,550 _____

Write each number in word form.

14 347

_____

15 103

_____

16 522

_____

17 931

_____

Solve.

18 **PUZZLES**   Use the digits 7, 9, and 8 to write the greatest number possible. Use each digit only once. _____

19 **PUZZLES**   Use the digits 3, 9, and 5 to write the least number possible. Use each digit only once. _____

20 **BANKING**   Alvin needs to make a code for his ATM card. He wants to use the digits 3, 7, 9, and 2. He also wants the number to be the greatest combination of these numbers. What four-digit number should he use as his code? _____

Copyright © by The McGraw-Hill Companies, Inc.

Compare and Order Whole Numbers Less Than 10,000

KEY Concept

You can use a number line to compare numbers, such as 2,100 and 2,700.

- The greatest numbers are farthest right on the number line. The least numbers are farthest left on the number line.

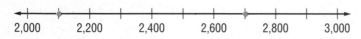

2,100 is left of 2,700   2,700 is right of 2,100

2,100 is less than 2,700   2,700 is greater than 2,100

Write 2,100 < 2,700   Write 2,700 > 2,100

You can use a place value chart to order numbers from greatest to least, or least to greatest.

2,137   2,839

Start at the left of each number and compare each place value.

1000	100	10	1
thousands	hundreds	tens	ones
2	①	3	7
2	⑧	3	9

Compare numbers 1 and 8.
1 < 8, and 8 > 1.

The value in the thousands place is the same. Move to the next number.

Order from greatest to least: 2,839; 2,137

Order from least to greatest: 2,137; 2,839

VOCABULARY

greater than (>)
an inequality relationship showing that the number on the left side of the symbol is greater than the number on the right side

less than (<)
an inequality relationship showing that the number on the left side of the symbol is less than the number on the right side

Use the **greater than** symbol (>) or **less than** symbol (<) to write statements that compare numbers.

Copyright © by The McGraw-Hill Companies, Inc.

Example 1

Use <, =, or > to compare 1,450 and 1,360.

1. Write both numbers in a place-value chart.

1000	100	10	1
thousands	hundreds	tens	ones
1	4	5	0
1	3	6	0

2. Begin on the left. Compare the digits in the thousands places. **1 = 1**

3. Compare the digits in the hundreds places.　　　　**4 > 3**

4. Because the digits in the hundreds places are different, there is no need to compare the other digits.

5. Write a statement using the > symbol.　　　**1,450 > 1,360**

YOUR TURN!

Use <, =, or > to compare 7,675 and 7,687.

1. Write both numbers in a place-value chart.

1000	100	10	1
thousands	hundreds	tens	ones

2. Begin on the left. Compare the digits in the thousands places.

　　　　　　　　　_____

3. Compare the digits in the hundreds places.　　_____

4. Compare the digits in the tens places.　　_____

5. Because the digits in the tens places are different, there is no need to compare the other digits.

6. Write a statement using the correct symbol.

　　　　　　　_____

Example 2

Compare 1,600 and 1,900.

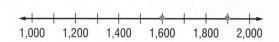

1. 1,600 is to the left of 1,900.

2. 1,900 is to the right of 1,600.

3. 1,600 is less than 1,900.　　**1,600 < 1,900**

Copyright © by The McGraw-Hill Companies, Inc.

GO ON

YOUR TURN!

Compare 3,675 and 3,400.

3,000   3,200   3,400   3,600   3,800   4,000

1. _____ is to the left of _____.

2. _____ is to the right of _____.

3. 3,675 is _____ than _____.   3,675 _____ 3,400.

Example 3

Order the numbers 2,385, 2,835, and 2,583 from greatest to least.

1. Underline each digit in the thousands place.   2,385   2,835   2,583

2. Since each value is the same, circle each
   digit in the hundreds place.   2,385   2,835   2,583

3. Compare 3, 5, and 8.   3 < 5   8 > 3   8 > 5

4. Use the hundreds place to order the numbers.
   2,835, 2,583, 2,385

YOUR TURN!

Order the numbers 8,659, 8,137, and 8,842 from least to greatest.

1. Underline each digit in the thousands
   place.   _____ _____ _____

2. Since each value is the same, circle each
   digit in the hundreds place.   _____ _____ _____

3. Compare _____, _____, and 8.   _____ _____ _____

4. Use the hundreds place to order the
   numbers.   _____, _____, _____

Copyright © by The McGraw-Hill Companies, Inc.

Who is Correct?

Compare 3,458 and 3,854.

Carisa
3,458 > 3,854

Molly
3,458 = 3,854

Tyron
3,458 < 3,854

Circle correct answer(s). Cross out incorrect answer(s).

 Guided Practice

1 Is 3,599 greater than or less than 4,000?

_____

2 Is 2,000 greater than or less than 1,902?

_____

Step by Step Practice

3 Order the numbers 2,529, 2,568, and 2,514 from greatest to least.

Step 1 Identify the place value you will use to compare the numbers. _____

Step 2 Write each number. Circle each digit in the _____ place. _____ _____ _____

Step 3 Compare the circled digits. Order the numbers from least to greatest. _____ _____ _____

Use <, =, or > to complete each statement.

4 1,304 _____ 1,615

5 4,129 _____ 2,749

6 2,607 _____ 2,099

7 9,280 _____ 9,270

Order from least to greatest.

8 3,785, 3,925, 3,548 _____, _____, _____

9 6,270, 6,720, 6,007 _____, _____, _____

10 1,928, 1,567, 1,114 _____, _____, _____

GO ON

Copyright © by The McGraw-Hill Companies, Inc.

Copyright © by The McGraw-Hill Companies, Inc.

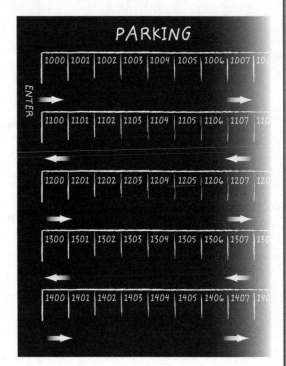

Problem-Solving Strategies

☐ Act it out.
☑ Make a diagram.
☐ Solve a simpler problem.
☐ Work backward.
☐ Use logical reasoning.

11 TRAVEL   At an airport parking garage, parking spaces are numbered using four-digit numbers. The first row of parking starts with 1000. Each row starts with 100 more than the row before it.

Ruri parked in the space numbered 1305. What is the number of the first parking space in her row?

Understand   Read the problem. Write what you know.

Ruri parked in space _____.

Plan   Pick a strategy. One strategy is to make a diagram.

Make a sketch of the parking garage rows.

Solve   Ruri's parking space is between 1,300 and 1,399. The space at the beginning of her row is 1,300.

Check   Create a number line labeled from 1,300 to 1,400. Graph 1,305 to verify your answer.

12 COMMUNITY   Orlando lives in apartment 2356. Monty lives in apartment 2382. Suppose you start at apartment 2300 and walk toward 2399. Whose apartment will you get to first?
Check off each step.

_____ Understand: I circled key words.

_____ Plan: To solve the problem, I will _____.

_____ Solve: The answer is _____.

_____ Check: I checked my answer by _____.

13 **Reflect** Explain how to compare 6,358 and 6,372.

_____

_____

 ## Skills, Concepts, and Problem Solving

Write _true_ or _false_ for each statement. If a statement is false, change the statement to make it true.

14 In a "greater than" inequality, the number on the left side is less than the number on the right side.

_____

_____

15 When comparing numbers, you look at the place value beginning at the left.

_____

_____

Use <, =, or > to complete each statement.

16 3,409 _____ 3,197

17 8,652 _____ 6,825

18 5,093 _____ 5,301

19 1,940 _____ 1,950

20 4,930 _____ 4,919

21 7,989 _____ 9,112

Order from greatest to least.

22 1,170; 1,750; 1,250

_____, _____, _____

23 2,102; 2,220; 2,021

_____, _____, _____

24 5,459; 5,945; 5,554

_____, _____, _____

25 8,452; 8,254; 8,524

_____, _____, _____

Order from least to greatest.

26 4,360; 4,120; 4,004

_____, _____, _____

27 9,231; 9,810; 9,475

_____, _____, _____

GO ON

Copyright © by The McGraw-Hill Companies, Inc.

28 1,952; 1,559; 1,295

29 2,002; 2,200; 2,020

_____, _____, _____

_____, _____, _____

Solve.

30 **NUMBER SENSE** The digits in Tiwa's street address are 7, 2, 5, and 8. Her address is the greatest possible even number. What is the number in Tiwa's address? _____

31 **PASSWORD** Harold wants to create a five-digit computer password. Suppose Harold uses the numbers 7, 3, 9, 8, and 4. What is the least possible password that Harold can create? Write your answer in expanded form.

_____

Vocabulary Check **Write the vocabulary word that completes each sentence.**

32 The > symbol is the _____ symbol.

33 The < symbol is the _____ symbol.

34 **Writing in Math** Given the digits 3, 5, 7, and 0, write 3 four-digit numbers. Use each digit once. Write the numbers from least to greatest. Explain how you compare four-digit numbers.

_____

_____

 Spiral Review

Write each number in standard form. (Lesson 1-1, p. 4)

35 eight hundred ninety-two _____

36 two hundred fifteen _____

37 four hundred six _____

38 one hundred twenty-five _____

Solve. (Lesson 1-2, p. 9)

39 **LITERATURE** The All Poems Publishing Group has poems to organize into a book. There are 4,000 funny poems, 500 nature poems, and 30 animal poems. How many poems will be in the book? _____

STOP

Copyright © by The McGraw-Hill Companies, Inc.

Whole Numbers to 100,000

KEY Concept

You can show a number in different ways:

standard form: in numbers

52,147

expanded form: an addition sentence

50,000 + 2,000 + 100 + 40 + 7

word form: in words

fifty-two thousand, one hundred forty-seven

Place values are grouped into periods. Each **period** has hundreds, tens, and ones places.

VOCABULARY

place value
the value given to a digit by its position in a number

standard form
writing a number using only digits

expanded form
writing a number as a sum that shows the value of each digit

word form
writing numbers using only words

period
a group of three digits in the place-value chart

Example 1

Read and write 42,178 in word form.

1. Read the first period. forty-two thousand

2. Read the second period. one hundred seventy-eight

3. Write the word form.
   forty-two thousand, one hundred seventy-eight

thousands		ones		
10,000	1,000	100	10	1
ten thousands	thousands	hundreds	tens	ones
4	2	1	7	8

YOUR TURN!

Read and write 51,342 in word form.

1. Read the first period. _____

2. Read the second period. _____

3. Write the word form. _____

thousands		ones		
10,000	1,000	100	10	1
ten thousands	thousands	hundreds	tens	ones
5	1	3	4	2

GO ON

Copyright © by The McGraw-Hill Companies, Inc.

Example 2

Identify the value of the underlined digit in 7̲5,310.

1. Write the number in a place-value chart.

2. The underlined digit is in the **ten-thousands** place.

3. Replace all the numbers to the right of the underlined digit with zeros.

4. The underlined digit has a value of **70,000**.

10,000 ten thousands	1,000 thousands	100 hundreds	10 tens	1 ones
7	5	3	1	0
7	0	0	0	0

YOUR TURN!

Identify the value of the underlined digit in 44̲,962.

1. Write the number in a place-value chart.

2. In what place is the underlined digit?

_____

3. Replace all the numbers to the right of the underlined digit with zeros.

4. What is the value of the underlined digit? _____

10,000 ten thousands	1,000 thousands	100 hundreds	10 tens	1 ones

Example 3

Write 85,261 in expanded form.

1. Write the numbers in a place-value chart.

2. Write the value of each digit.

10,000 ten thousands	1,000 thousands	100 hundreds	10 tens	1 ones
8	5	2	6	1

$$8 \rightarrow 8 \times 10,000 = 80,000$$
$$5 \rightarrow 5 \times 1,000 = 5,000$$
$$2 \rightarrow 2 \times 100 = 200$$
$$6 \rightarrow 6 \times 10 = 60$$
$$1 \rightarrow 1 \times 1 = 1$$

3. Write the expanded form of 85,261. **80,000 + 5,000 + 200 + 60 + 1**

YOUR TURN!

Write 23,914 in expanded form.

1. Write the numbers in a place-value chart.

2. Write the value of each digit.

3. Write the expanded form of 23,914. _____

10,000 ten thousands	1,000 thousands	100 hundreds	10 tens	1 ones

Copyright © by The McGraw-Hill Companies, Inc.

Who is Correct?

Write the standard form for six hundred two thousand, ninety-seven.

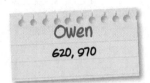
Owen
620,970

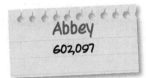
Abbey
602,097

Grant
6,297

Circle correct answer(s). Cross out incorrect answer(s).

 Guided Practice

Read and write the numbers in word form.

1 37,879

_____ thousand, _____

2 41,205

_____ thousand, _____

Step by Step Practice

3 **Write 39,604 in expanded form.**

Step 1 Write the numbers in a place-value chart.

Step 2 Write the value of each digit.

Step 3 Write the expanded form of 39,604.

_____

10,000	1,000	100	10	1
ten thousands	thousands	hundreds	tens	ones

Write each number in expanded form.

4 42,823 _____ + _____ + _____ + _____ + _____

5 11,739 _____

Copyright © by The McGraw-Hill Companies, Inc.

GO ON

Solve.

Problem-Solving Strategies
☐ Draw a model.
☐ Use logical reasoning.
☐ Make a table.
☑ Solve a simpler problem.
☐ Work backward.

6 MOON The Moon is two hundred thirty-eight thousand, seven hundred twelve miles from Earth. Write the number in standard form.

Understand	Read the problem. Write what you know.
	There are _____ periods, or groups of hundreds, tens, and ones in the number.
Plan	Pick a strategy. One strategy is solving a simpler problem.
Solve	Separate the number into the thousands period and the ones period.
	Write the thousands period in digits. _____
	Write the ones period in digits. _____
	Write the periods together, separated by a comma. _____
Check	Read the standard form aloud. Follow along with the word form to make sure the forms match.

7 DISTANCE Nikki lives in Oklahoma. Her cousin Tara lives one thousand, four hundred eighteen miles away in Florida. Write the distance between the two cousins in standard form. Check off each step.

_____ Understand: I circled key words.

_____ Plan: To solve the problem, I will _____.

_____ Solve: The answer is _____.

_____ Check: I will check my answer by _____.

8 NUMBERS As his father read numbers aloud, Dario wrote them out in word form. Dario's father read 86,293. How should Dario write this number?

Copyright © by The McGraw-Hill Companies, Inc.

9 **Reflect** Explain the difference between the standard form and expanded form of a number.

_____

_____

▶ Skills, Concepts, and Problem Solving

Write each number in word form.

10 92,531 _____

11 45,369 _____

12 80,467 _____

13 63,142 _____

Identify the value of the underlined digit.

14 3<u>3</u>,252 _____ **15** 46,<u>8</u>15 _____

16 <u>7</u>1,957 _____ **17** 15,48<u>2</u> _____

18 27,1<u>5</u>8 _____ **19** <u>8</u>1,510 _____

Write each number in expanded form.

20 26,495 _____

21 51,316 _____

22 99,212 _____

23 68,425 _____

24 **FISH** The marine biologist estimated the school of fish to be 86,250 fish. How would she write this number in expanded form?

_____

Copyright © by The McGraw-Hill Companies, Inc.

GO ON

25 BANKING Mr. Thomas works in a bank. He has to write numbers from bank statements in word form. How would he write the number 36,739 in word form?

_____

Vocabulary Check **Write the vocabulary word that completes each sentence.**

26 Writing a number using only digits is called

_____.

27 A group of three digits in the place value chart is called a

_____.

28 _____ is the value given to a digit by its position in a number.

29 Writing in Math Vincent wanted to write 48,320 in word form. He wrote "four thousand, eight hundred thirty-two." Explain Vincent's mistake.

_____

_____

_____

▶ **Spiral Review**

Identify the value of the underlined digit. (Lessons 1-1, p. 4 and 1-2, p. 9)

30 3<u>5</u>9 _____

31 <u>9</u>,428 _____

Write <, =, or > to complete each statement. (Lesson 1-3, p. 16)

32 2,519 ◯ 3,057

33 5,630 ◯ 5,919

34 8,445 ◯ 8,415

35 3,112 ◯ 3,101

STOP

Copyright © by The McGraw-Hill Companies, Inc.

Progress Check 2 (Lessons 1-3 and 1-4)

Use <, =, or > to complete each statement.

1 2,750 ( ) 2,570

2 3,498 ( ) 3,682

3 5,193 ( ) 5,624

4 4,328 ( ) 4,238

5 3,178 ( ) 3,194

6 8,629 ( ) 8,610

Write each number in expanded form.

7 1,802 _____

8 3,461 _____

9 7,015 _____

10 9,060 _____

Identify the value of the underlined digit.

11 23,452 _____

12 78,910 _____

13 54,138 _____

14 15,762 _____

Solve.

15 **PUZZLES** Use the digits 6, 8, and 5 to write the least possible odd number. Use each digit once.

_____

16 **BANKING** Mrs. Glover needs to make a code for her ATM card. She wants to use the digits 1, 7, 9, and 2. She also wants the number to be odd. What is the largest four-digit number Mrs. Glover can use as her code?

_____

17 **SHOPPING** Diego is shopping at three stores. The bicycle shop address is 1592. The sporting goods shop address is 1796. The health food shop address is 1284. Order the shop addresses from least to greatest.

_____, _____, _____

Copyright © by The McGraw-Hill Companies, Inc.

Patterns

Copyright © by The McGraw-Hill Companies, Inc.

KEY Concept

A **pattern** is a sequence of numbers or shapes that repeats according to a **rule**. To find a pattern, follow these steps.

1. Say each number or shape out loud.
2. Listen for the **terms** of the pattern that repeat.
3. Use the terms of the pattern that repeat to find the next term.

1, 2, 3, 1, 2, 3, 1, 2, 3

The next term in the pattern is 1.

To complete this pattern of shapes, the next shape must complete the repeating part of the pattern and then the pattern starts over again.

The next three shapes in the pattern are .

VOCABULARY

pattern
a sequence of numbers, shapes, or symbols that follows a rule or design
Example: 2, 4, 6, 8

rule
tells how numbers or figures are related to each other

terms
each of the quantities that forms a series or pattern

Example 1

What is the pattern? Write the next term in the pattern.

A, A, B, A, A, B, A, A, B
├--------┼---------┼--------┤

1. Read the pattern out loud.

2. The repeating terms are A, A, B. This is the pattern.

3. Use the terms of the pattern that repeat to find the next term.

The next term is A.

YOUR TURN!

What is the pattern? Write the next term in the pattern.

5, 10, 10, 5, 10, 10, 5, 10, 10
├----------┼-----------┼-----------┤

1. Read the pattern out loud.

2. The repeating terms are _____, _____, _____.

3. Use the terms of the pattern that repeat to find the next term.

The next term is _____.

Example 2

What is the pattern? Write the next three terms in the pattern.

|--------|--------|--------|------

1. Read the pattern out loud.

2. The repeating terms are "square, circle, circle." This is the pattern.

3. Use the terms of the pattern that repeat to find the next term.

A circle is needed to complete the repeating terms. Then begin the repeating terms again.

The next term is ⬤, followed by ⬛, ⬤.

YOUR TURN!

What is the pattern? Write the next three terms in the pattern.

|----------------|----------------|--

1. Read the pattern out loud.

2. The repeating terms are _____, _____, _____, _____, _____.

3. Use the terms of the pattern that repeat to find the next term.

Another _____ circle is next, followed by two _____ circles.

Who is Correct?

What is the next term in the pattern?

X, Y, Y, Z, X, Y, Y, Z, X, Y

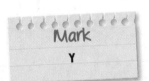

Circle correct answer(s). Cross out incorrect answer(s).

▶ Guided Practice

List the repeating terms of each pattern.

1. 4, 3, 3, 3, 4, 3, 3, 3 _____

2. M, M, N, N, M, M, N, N _____

3.  _____

4   What is the pattern? Write the next term in the pattern.
21, 22, 22, 21, 22, 22, 21, 22

   Step 1   Read the pattern out loud.

   Step 2   The repeating terms are _____, _____, _____.

   Step 3   Use the terms of the pattern that repeat to find the
   next term. The number _____ is needed to
   complete the repeating terms.

   The next term is _____.

What is the pattern? Write the next term in each pattern.

5   A, a, B, b, A, a, B, b, A, a

The repeating terms are _____, _____, _____, _____.

The letters _____, _____ are needed to complete the
repeating terms.

The next term is _____.

6

The repeating terms are _____, _____, _____, _____.

The next term is _____.

What is the pattern? Write the next three terms in each pattern.

7   r, S, t, T, t, r, S, t, T, t, r

The repeating terms are _____, _____, _____, _____, _____.

The next three terms are _____, _____, _____.

8

The repeating terms are _____, _____, _____.

The next three terms are _____, _____, _____.

Copyright © by The McGraw-Hill Companies, Inc.

Step by Step Problem-Solving Practice

Solve.

Problem-Solving Strategies
☐ Draw a diagram.
☑ Look for a pattern.
☐ Guess and check.
☐ Act it out.
☐ Work backward.

9 **SCHOOL**   Tim's English grades for the first four weeks of school are listed below. If this pattern continues, what will be the 23rd grade Tim will receive in English?
B, B, C, A, B, B, C, A, B, B, C

Understand   Read the problem. Write what you know.
Tim's English grades were _____, _____, _____, _____, _____, _____, _____, _____, _____, _____, _____

Plan   Pick a strategy. One strategy is to look for a pattern.

Solve   The repeating pattern is _____, _____, _____, _____.

According to the pattern, the 23rd grade Tim will receive is a(n) _____.

Check   Look at the pattern. Does your answer follow the pattern?

10 **LANDSCAPING**   While shopping for flowers, Simona noticed that the florist had displays arranged by color. In this pattern of flower colors, which color is missing? Check off each step.

_____ Understand: I circled key words.

_____ Plan: To solve the problem, I will _____.

_____ Solve: The answer is _____.

_____ Check: I checked my answer by _____.

Copyright © by The McGraw-Hill Companies, Inc.

GO ON

11 WEATHER   Wilma recorded the weather pattern shown below for the last eight days. The weather reporter predicted rain on Sunday. Will rain on Sunday follow Wilma's pattern? Explain.

_____

Sat   Sun   Mon   Tue   Wed   Thu   Fri   Sat   Sun   ?

12 **Reflect**   Is the next number in the pattern 5? Explain.

5, 55, 505, 5, 5, 55, 505, 5

_____

_____

▶ Skills, Concepts, and Problem Solving

Write the repeating terms of each pattern.

13   10, 100, 100, 10, 100, 100 _____

14   X, x, y, Y, X, x, y, Y _____

15   △ ▲ ▲ △ △ ▲ ▲ △   _____

16   3, 4, 4, 5, 6, 7, 3, 4, 4, 5, 6, 7 _____

What is the pattern? Write the next term in each pattern.

17   20, 2, 2, 20, 20, 2, 2, 20

The repeating terms are _____, _____, _____, _____.

The next term is _____.

18   ★ ⬆ ★ ⬇ ★ ⬆ ★ ⬇

The repeating terms are _____, _____, _____, _____.

The next term is _____.

Copyright © by The McGraw-Hill Companies, Inc.

What is the pattern? Write the next three terms in each pattern.

19 J, k, L, J, k, L, J

The next three terms are _____, _____, _____.

20 10, 101, 101, 10, 10, 10, 101, 101, 10, 10

The next three terms are _____, _____, _____.

Solve.

21 TRAVEL   To travel from Phil's Pharmacy to Betty's Bagels, there are 10 turns. Ivan noticed a pattern.

If the pattern continues, what is the 10th turn to Betty's Bagels?

_____

22 NOTEBOOKS   Katrina was doodling in her notebook. She made the following pattern of marks. What is the next mark that Katrina will make in her notebook if she continues the pattern?

_____

23 CAFETERIA   The school lunch menu has a pattern.

Monday	Tuesday	Wednesday	Thursday	Friday
chicken fingers	hamburgers	pizza	chicken fingers	hamburgers

If this pattern continues next week, what will be served next Wednesday? _____

Copyright © by The McGraw-Hill Companies, Inc.

GO ON

24 MUSIC In a musical piece for the school marching band, the trumpets play these notes:

E F G E E F G E E

If the pattern continues, what are the next three notes?

_____, _____, _____

Vocabulary Check **Write the vocabulary word that completes each sentence.**

25 A(n) _____ is a sequence of numbers, figures, or symbols that follows a rule or design.

26 _____ are the quantities that form a sequence or pattern.

27 Writing in Math Explain how the patterns in problems 12 and 14 were similar.

_____

_____

> **Spiral Review**

Write each number in expanded form. (Lessons 1-1, p.4 and 1-2, p. 9)

28 908 _____

29 204 _____

30 1,367 _____

31 4,972 _____

32 two hundred seven

33 five thousand eight hundred forty-three

_____

_____

Identify the value of the underlined digit. (Lessons 1-2, p.9 and 1-4, p. 23)

34 2,<u>7</u>02 _____

35 <u>3</u>00,594 _____

36 20<u>3</u>,000 _____

37 9,2<u>6</u>0 _____

38 7,5<u>5</u>0 _____

39 <u>3</u>5,689 _____

Copyright © by The McGraw-Hill Companies, Inc.

STOP

Number Patterns

Copyright © by The McGraw-Hill Companies, Inc.

KEY Concept

0 1 2 3 4 5 6 7 8 9 10 11 12

Even numbers are any whole numbers that have been multiplied by 2. The last digit of the number will be a 0, 2, 4, 6, or 8. Zero is an even number. Even numbers are shown in red above.

Odd numbers are not multiples of 2. The last digit of the number will be a 1, 3, 5, 7, or 9. Odd numbers are shown in blue above.

A **number pattern** is a repeating sequence of numbers.

VOCABULARY

even number
a number that can be divided by 2

number pattern
a regular and repeating sequence of numbers

odd number
a number that cannot be divided evenly by 2; such a number has 1, 3, 5, 7, or 9 in the ones place

Number patterns can be shown on number lines or written as a list.

Example 1

Graph the even whole numbers that are less than 8.

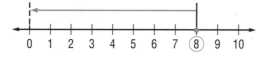

0 1 2 3 4 5 6 7 ⑧ 9 10

1. Locate 8 on the number line and circle it.

2. Draw an arrow in the direction that will show numbers less than 8.

3. There is an even number before and after every odd number. From 8, moving left, skip over a number, and place a dot on 6. Place dots on the numbers 4, 2, and 0.

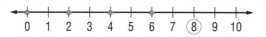

0 1 2 3 4 5 6 7 ⑧ 9 10

YOUR TURN!

Graph the odd whole numbers that are less than 9.

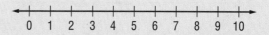

0 1 2 3 4 5 6 7 8 9 10

1. Locate 9 on the number line and circle it.

2. Draw an arrow in the direction that will show numbers less than 9.

   Is it to the left or right of 9 on the number line? _____

3. There is an odd number before and after every even number. From 9, place a dot on every odd number less than 9.

GO ON

Example 2

Complete the number pattern.
11, 14, 17, _____, 23
Explain the pattern.

1. Graph the numbers on a number line.

2. To get from 11 to 14, count to the right three numbers. You count right three numbers to get from 14 to 17.

3. Graph the missing point in the pattern.

20 is 3 units to the right of 17.

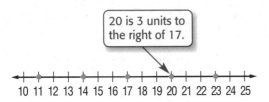

4. Complete the pattern.
   11, 14, 17, _20_, 23

5. Explain the pattern.
   Add 3 to each number.

YOUR TURN!

Complete the number pattern.
19, 16, 13, _____, 7
Explain the pattern.

1. Graph the numbers on a number line.

```
   5 6 7 8 9 10 11 12 13 14 15 16 17 18 19 20
```

2. How many numbers are there from 19 to 16? _____
   Did you count to the right or left of 19? _____
   How many numbers are there from 16 to 13? _____

3. On the number line above, graph the missing point in the pattern.

4. Complete the pattern.
   19, 16, 13, _____, 7

5. Explain the pattern.
   _____

Who is Correct?

Complete the pattern.

70, 75, 80, _____, 90

Rashelle
70, 75, 80, 95, 90

Cedro
70, 75, 80, 75, 90

Tanika
70, 75, 80, 85, 90

Circle correct answer(s). Cross out incorrect answer(s).

Copyright © by The McGraw-Hill Companies, Inc.

▶ Guided Practice

1 Numbers that end in 1, 3, 5, 7, and 9 are called _____ numbers.

2 Whole numbers that end in 0, 2, 4, 6, and 8 are called _____ numbers.

For each number, write *even* or *odd*.

3 68 _____

4 99 _____

5 29 _____

6 44 _____

Step by Step Practice

7 Graph the even whole numbers greater than 3 on the number line.

> Remember: Even numbers are multiples of 2. Odd numbers are not.

Step 1 Locate _____ on the number line.

Step 2 Numbers greater than 3 are to the _____ on the number line.

Step 3 The number _____ is even and closest to 3.

Step 4 Graph the even numbers greater than 3 on the number line.

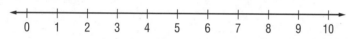

Graph the even whole numbers on the number line.

8 between 5 and 10

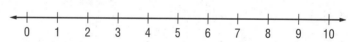

9 counting numbers less than 9

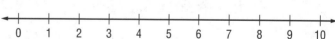

Complete each number pattern. Explain the pattern.

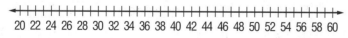

20 22 24 26 28 30 32 34 36 38 40 42 44 46 48 50 52 54 56 58 60

10 24, 26, 28, _____, 32

_____

11 35, 40, 45, _____, 55

_____

12 24, 27, 30, _____, 36

_____

13 42, 40, 38, _____, 34

_____

GO ON

Copyright © by The McGraw-Hill Companies, Inc.

Solve.

Problem-Solving Strategies
☑ Draw a graph.
☐ Guess and check.
☐ Act it out.
☐ Make a table.
☐ Solve a simpler problem.

14 **PUZZLES**   I am an even whole number that is less than 6 and greater than 3. What number am I?

Understand   Read the problem. Write what you know.

The number is greater than _____.

The number is less than _____.

Plan   Pick a strategy. One strategy is to draw a graph. Create a number line. Label it from 0 to 8.

Solve   Locate 6 on the number line. Draw an arrow from the 6 pointing to the numbers that are less than 6.

Locate 3. Draw an arrow from the 3 pointing to the numbers that are greater than 3.

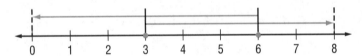

The only even number between 3 and 6 is 4. The number is _____.

Check   Is 4 less than 6? _____

Is 4 greater than 3? _____

The number 4 solves the puzzle.

15 **PUZZLES**   I am an odd counting number that is between 18 and 20. What number am I? Check off each step.

_____ Understand: I circled key words.

_____ Plan: To solve the problem, I will _____.

_____ Solve: The answer is _____.

_____ Check: I checked my answer by _____.

Copyright © by The McGraw-Hill Companies, Inc.

16 **PUZZLES** I am an even whole number that is less than 44 and more than 38. My last digit is a 0. What number am I? _____

17 **Reflect** Name the first even whole number. Draw a number line to explain your answer.

_____

_____

▶ Skills, Concepts, and Problem Solving

Write *true* or *false* for each statement. If a statement is false, change the statement to make it true.

18 The first even whole number is zero.

_____

19 The first odd counting number is zero.

_____

For each number, write *even* or *odd*.

20 51 _____ **21** 98 _____ **22** 27 _____

23 33 _____ **24** 0 _____ **25** 100 _____

Graph the numbers on a number line.

26 odd whole numbers that are less than 6

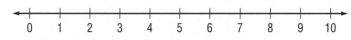

27 even whole numbers that are less than 6

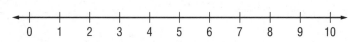

28 odd counting numbers between 23 and 30

29 even counting numbers between 21 and 27

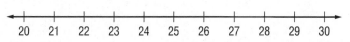

GO ON

Copyright © by The McGraw-Hill Companies, Inc.

Complete each number pattern. Explain the number pattern.

```
0  2  4  6  8  10 12 14 16 18 20 22 24 26 28 30 32 34 36 38 40 42 44 46 48 50 52 54 56 58 60
```

30 44, 46, 48, _____, 52 _____

31 35, 40, 45, _____, 55 _____

32 60, 50, 40, _____, 20 _____

33 60, 55, 50, _____, 40 _____

34 25, 21, 17, _____, 9 _____

35 7, 14, 21, _____, 35 _____

Write the missing even numbers.

36 1, ____, 3, ____, 5, ____, 7, ____, 9

37 45, ____, 47, ____, 49, ____, 51, ____

38 33, ____, 35, ____, 37, ____, 39, ____

39 51, ____, 53, ____, 55, ____, 57, ____

Write the missing odd numbers.

40 22, ____, 24, ____, 26, ____, 28, ____

41 44, ____, 46, ____, 48, ____, 50, ____

42 52, ____, 54, ____, 56, ____, 58, ____

43 28, ____, 30, ____, 32, ____, 34, ____

Solve.

44 PUZZLES   I am an even whole number that is less than 26 and more than 23. What number am I?

_____

45 PUZZLES   I am an odd counting number that is between 45 and 50. One digit is a 9. What number am I?

_____

46 PUZZLES   I am an even whole number that is less than 84 and more than 79. My last digit is a 0. What number am I?

_____

Copyright © by The McGraw-Hill Companies, Inc.

47 **PUZZLES**   I am an odd whole number that is less than 84 and more than 79. My last digit is a 1. What number am I?

_____

Vocabulary Check   **Write the vocabulary word that completes each sentence.**

48 Numbers that are used to count objects are the

_____.

49 Numbers that are divisible by 2 are _____ numbers.

50 **Writing in Math**   Explain the difference between even and odd whole numbers.

_____

_____

_____

▶ **Spiral Review**

Write the repeating terms of each pattern. (Lesson 1-5, p. 30)

51 ⬜⬠○○⬠⬜○○   _____

52 1, 11, 111, 1, 11, 111 _____

53 8, 80, 808, 8, 80, 808 _____

Solve. (Lesson 1-3, p. 16)

54 **CHECKS**   Fidel is learning how to write checks. His father tells him to write the check for $5,472. How should Fidel write the number in word form?

_____

Copyright © by The McGraw-Hill Companies, Inc.

Complete each number pattern. Explain the number pattern.

1 9, 19, 29, _____, 49 _____

2 84, 87, 90, _____, 96 _____

3 32, 30, 28, _____, 24 _____

4 14, 20, 26, _____, 38 _____

5 16, 14, 12, _____, 8 _____

6 50, 55, 60, _____, 70 _____

Write the repeating terms of each pattern.

7 K, K, j, J, j, K, K, j, J, j _____

8 _____

What is the pattern? Write the next term in the pattern.

9 9, 90, 909, 9, 90, 909, 9, 90

The repeating terms are _____, _____, _____.

The next term is _____.

10

The repeating terms are _____, _____, _____, _____, _____.

The next term is _____.

Solve.

11 **PUZZLES** I am an odd whole number between 32 and 35. What number am I? _____

12 **PUZZLES** I am an even counting number between 18 and 21. What number am I? _____

13 **NEIGHBORHOODS** Driving down his road, Andrew noticed that the front doors on the houses were painted using a color pattern. The door colors were blue, brown, red, red, blue, brown, red. If the pattern continues, what color should Andrew see on the next door?

_____

Copyright © by The McGraw-Hill Companies, Inc.

Vocabulary and Concept Check

digit, *p. 4*

even number, *p. 37*

expanded form, *p. 4*

greater than, *p. 16*

less than, *p. 16*

number pattern, *p. 37*

odd number, *p. 37*

pattern, *p. 30*

place value, *p. 4*

rule, *p. 30*

standard form, *p. 4*

terms, *p. 30*

word form, *p. 4*

Write the vocabulary word that completes each sentence.

1 Any number that can be divided by 2 is a(n) _____.

2 _____ are numbers or quantities that form a series or pattern.

3 The numbers 0, 1, 2, 3, 4, 5, 6, 7, 8, and 9 are called _____.

4 The > symbol shows that the number on the left of the symbol is _____ the number on the right.

Label each diagram below. Write the correct place value in each blank.

5 _____

↓

23,496

6 _____

↓

19,650

Lesson Review

1-1 Whole Numbers to 1,000 (pp. 4–8)

Write each number in standard form.

7 five hundred fourteen _____

8 two hundred seventy-six _____

9 nine hundred nine _____

10 three hundred forty-eight _____

Example 1

Write seven hundred sixty-two in standard form.

There are 7 hundreds in the number. There are 6 tens in the number. There are 2 ones in the number.

The number in standard form is 762.

100	10	1
hundreds	tens	ones
7	6	2

Copyright © by The McGraw-Hill Companies, Inc.

1-2 Whole Numbers Less Than 10,000 (pp. 9–14)

Identify the value of each underlined digit.

11. 2,753 _____

12. 9,040 _____

13. 2,948 _____

14. 6,054 _____

15. 1,181 _____

16. 5,805 _____

Example 2

Identify the value of the underlined digit in 3,5̲06.

Write each digit in the place-value chart.

The underlined digit is in the hundreds place.

Multiply the underlined digit by the value of its place. $5 \times 100 = 500$

1000 thousands	100 hundreds	10 tens	1 ones
3	5	0	6

The underlined digit has a value of 500.

1-3 Compare and Order Whole Numbers Less Than 10,000 (pp. 16–22)

Use <, =, or > to complete each statement.

17. 8,600 ◯ 8,006

18. 9,250 ◯ 9,520

19. 1,781 ◯ 2,407

20. 4,129 ◯ 3,991

Example 3

Use <, =, or > to compare 5,475 and 5,575.

Begin on the left. Compare the digits in the thousands place. $5 = 5$

Compare the digits in the hundreds place. $4 < 5$

1000 thousands	100 hundreds	10 tens	1 ones
5	4	7	5
5	5	7	5

Since 4 is less than 5, 5,475 is less than 5,575.

Write a statement using the < symbol. $5{,}475 < 5{,}575$

Copyright © by The McGraw-Hill Companies, Inc.

1-4 Whole Numbers to 100,000
(pp. 23–28)

Identify the value of the underlined digit.

21 44,172 _____

22 37,598 _____

23 81,629 _____

24 72,511 _____

Example 4

Identify the value of the underlined digit in 2̲5,170.

1. The underlined digit is in the **ten thousands** place.

2. Replace all the numbers to the right of the underlined digit with zeros.

3. The underlined digit has a value of **20,000**.

1-5 Patterns (pp. 30–36)

What are the patterns? Write the next term in each pattern.

25 F, G, H, H, F, G, H, H, …
The repeating terms are

_____.
The next term is _____.

26 1, 2, 2, 4, 1, 1, 2, 2, 4, 1, 1, …
The repeating terms are

_____.
The next term is _____.

Example 5

What is the pattern? Write the next term in the pattern.

X, Y, Y, X, Y, Y, X, Y, Y, X, Y, _____.

The repeating terms are X, Y, Y. This is the pattern. Use the terms of the pattern that repeat to find the next term.

The next term is Y.

1-6 Number Patterns (pp. 37-43)

Complete each number pattern.

27 26, 29, 32, 35, _____, 41

28 57, 55, 53, 51, _____, 47

29 3, 10, 17, _____, 31

30 81, 72, 63, 54, _____, 36

Example 6

Complete the number pattern.

16, 18, 20, _____, 24

15 16 17 18 19 20 21 22 23 24 25

To get from 16 to 18, count to the right **two** numbers. To get from 18 to 20, count to the right **two** numbers.

Complete the pattern. 16, 18, 20, 22, 24

Copyright © by The McGraw-Hill Companies, Inc.

Chapter Test

GO ON

Write each number in standard form.

1 seven hundred forty-six _____

2 two hundred eight _____

3 one hundred forty-two _____

4 six hundred eleven _____

5 2,000 + 800 + 50 + 9 _____

6 8,000 + 500 + 20 + 1 _____

Write each number in expanded form.

7 475 _____

8 609 _____

9 23 _____

10 172 _____

11 7,944 _____

12 4,707 _____

Identify the value of each underlined digit.

13 76,7̲90 _____

14 4̲,050 _____

15 5̲3,492 _____

16 8,04̲1 _____

17 7,93̲5 _____

18 21,1̲04 _____

Use <, = , or > to complete each statement.

19 9,430 ◯ 9,440

20 7,505 ◯ 7,055

21 3,856 ◯ 3,865

22 5,422 ◯ 5,242

Write each set of numbers in order from greatest to least.

23 4,250; 4,520; 4,500; 4,200 _____

24 8,458; 8,657; 8,511; 8,629 _____

25 6,321; 6,124; 6,787; 6,050 _____

26 3,756; 3,244; 3,118; 3,599 _____

Copyright © by The McGraw-Hill Companies, Inc.

List the repeating terms of each pattern.

27 G, H, i, i, Z, z, G, H, i, i, Z, z

_____

28 ☆★★☆★★

_____

What is the pattern? Write the next term in the pattern.

29 ☀ ☾ ★ ☀ ☀ ☾ ★ ☀

The repeating terms are _____.

The next term is _____.

Complete each number pattern. Explain the number pattern.

30 31, 27, 23, _____, 15

_____

31 43, 48, 53, _____, 63

_____

32 16, 22, 28, _____, 40

_____

Solve.

33 **LANDSCAPING** Green Acres Landscaping planted flowers in a certain order for the city of Hillshire. They planted the flowers in the color pattern shown below. If the pattern continues, what color should the next flowers be? _____

Correct the mistakes.

34 When the Quilt Club made a quilt, they used the pattern of squares shown at the right. When Ms. Franco asked Sashi to continue the pattern, Sashi sewed this square: ■

What was her mistake?

_____

Copyright © by The McGraw-Hill Companies, Inc.

STOP

Choose the best answer and fill in the corresponding circle on the sheet at right.

1 Which number shows nine hundred three written in standard form?

  A 903   **C** 930

  B 913   **D** 933

2 Which symbol makes this sentence true?

$$8,540 \,\square\, 8,450$$

  A >   **C** <

  B =   **D** +

3 $5,000 + 80 + 4 =$

  A 584   **C** 5,804

  B 5,084   **D** 5,884

4 Which of these is the number 88,753?

  A eighty thousand, seven fifty-three

  B eighty thousand, seven hundred fifty-three

  C eighty-eight hundred, seven hundred fifty-three

  D eighty-eight thousand, seven hundred fifty-three

5 Which number shows seven thousand, one hundred fifteen in standard form?

  A 7,100   **C** 7,150

  B 7,115   **D** 7,715

6 Which list is written in order from greatest to least?

  A 2,500; 2,520; 2,250; 2,200

  B 6,787; 6,124; 6,321; 6,050

  C 3,756; 3,599; 3,244; 3,118

  D 8,458; 8,511; 8,629; 8,657

7 Which digit is in the thousands place in 97,316?

  A 1

  B 3

  C 6

  D 7

8 What is the next figure in this pattern?

  A ◯

  B ◺

  C ▱

  D ◣

GO ON

Copyright © by The McGraw-Hill Companies, Inc.

9 Which are the repeating terms for the following pattern?
3, 33, 303, 3, 3, 33, 303, 3

    A 3, 33, 303, 3

    B 3, 3, 33, 303

    C 33, 303, 3, 33

    D 303, 33, 3, 3

10 The numbers in the pattern decrease by the same amount each time. What are the next three numbers in this pattern?
45, 39, 33, 27, 21, _____, _____, _____

    A 16, 11, 6   C 15, 9, 3

    B 20, 16, 12   D 15, 10, 5

11 Which is the rule for the number pattern?
23, 20, 17, 14, 11, 8, 5, 2

    A add 4

    B subtract 3

    C subtract 4

    D add 5

12 Which number is missing from the pattern?
23, 28, 33, _____, 43

    A 13   C 38

    B 18   D 48

Copyright © by The McGraw-Hill Companies, Inc.

ANSWER SHEET

Directions: Fill in the circle of each correct answer.

1	Ⓐ	Ⓑ	Ⓒ	Ⓓ
2	Ⓐ	Ⓑ	Ⓒ	Ⓓ
3	Ⓐ	Ⓑ	Ⓒ	Ⓓ
4	Ⓐ	Ⓑ	Ⓒ	Ⓓ
5	Ⓐ	Ⓑ	Ⓒ	Ⓓ
6	Ⓐ	Ⓑ	Ⓒ	Ⓓ
7	Ⓐ	Ⓑ	Ⓒ	Ⓓ
8	Ⓐ	Ⓑ	Ⓒ	Ⓓ
9	Ⓐ	Ⓑ	Ⓒ	Ⓓ
10	Ⓐ	Ⓑ	Ⓒ	Ⓓ
11	Ⓐ	Ⓑ	Ⓒ	Ⓓ
12	Ⓐ	Ⓑ	Ⓒ	Ⓓ

Success Strategy

Double check your answers after you finish. Read each problem and all of the answer choices. Put your finger on each bubble you filled in to make sure it matches the answer for each problem.

STOP

Multiplication

How much food does your dog eat?

Suppose your dog eats 2 pounds of dog food every day. How much dog food does your dog eat in a week? You can use multiplication to answer this question.

STEP 1 Quiz

Are you ready for Chapter 2? Take the Online Readiness Quiz at *macmillanmh.com* to find out.

STEP 2 Preview

Get ready for Chapter 2. Review these skills and compare them with what you will learn in this chapter.

What You Know	What You Will Learn
You know how to add. **Examples:** $2 + 2 + 2 = 6$ $5 + 5 = 10$ $10 + 10 + 10 + 10 = 40$ **TRY IT!** **1** $3 + 3 = $ _____ **2** $10 + 10 + 10 = $ _____ **3** $4 + 4 + 4 + 4 = $ _____	*Lesson 2-1* **Multiplication** is repeated addition. $2 \times 3 = \underbrace{2 + 2 + 2}_{\text{three 2s}} = 6$ $5 \times 2 = \underbrace{5 + 5}_{\text{two 5s}} = 10$ $10 \times 4 = \underbrace{10 + 10 + 10 + 10}_{\text{four 10s}} = 40$
You know how to skip count. **Example:** Skip count by 3s. 0, 3, 6, 9, 12, 15, 18, 21, 24, 27, 30, … **TRY IT!** **4** Skip count by 2s to 18. **5** Skip count by 5s to 40.	*Lessons 2-2 through 2-5* **Multiples** of 3 are the numbers you say when you skip count by 3s. 0, 3, 6, 9, 12, 15, 18, 21, 24, 27, … The multiples of 3 are the multiplication facts below. $0 \times 3 = 0 \qquad 5 \times 3 = 15$ $1 \times 3 = 3 \qquad 6 \times 3 = 18$ $2 \times 3 = 6 \qquad 7 \times 3 = 21$ $3 \times 3 = 9 \qquad 8 \times 3 = 24$ $4 \times 3 = 12 \qquad 9 \times 3 = 27$
You know that changing the order in which you add numbers does not change the sum. $1 + 7 = 8 \qquad 7 + 1 = 8$	*Lessons 2-3 through 2-5* $5 \times 3 = 15 \qquad 3 \times 5 = 15$ Changing the order in which you multiply numbers does not change the product.

53

Introduction to Multiplication

KEY Concept

The symbol × is used for multiplication.

factors   product

$$2 + 2 + 2 + 2 + 2 = 5 \times 2 = 10$$

repeated addition

You can model **multiplication** with an **array**.

2 × 5 is 2 groups of 5. Or, 5 × 2 is 5 groups of 2.

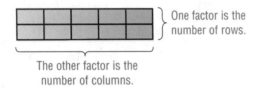

One factor is the number of rows.

The other factor is the number of columns.

The **product** is the total number of rectangles in the array.

$$2 \times 5 = 10$$

Another way to model 2 × 5 is with a number line.

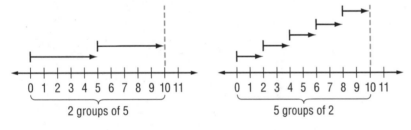

2 groups of 5   5 groups of 2

The product using either method is 10.

The order in which you multiply the numbers does not matter. So, 2 × 5 = 5 × 2.

VOCABULARY

array
an arrangement of objects or symbols in rows of the same length and columns of the same length; the length of a row might be different from the length of a column

factor
a number that divides into a whole number evenly; also a number that is multiplied by another number

factors   product

$$2 \times 3 = 6$$

multiplication
an operation on two numbers to find their product; it can be thought of as repeated addition Example: 4 × 3 is the same as the sum of four 3s, which is 3 + 3 + 3 + 3 or 12.

product
the answer or result of a multiplication problem; it also refers to expressing a number as the product of its factors

Copyright © by The McGraw-Hill Companies, Inc.

Example 1

Draw an array to model 6 × 3. Then write and model the related multiplication fact.

1. Identify the first factor. **6**
   This is the number of rows in the array.

2. Identify the second factor. **3**
   This is the number of columns in the array.

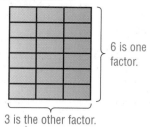

6 is one factor.

3 is the other factor.

   Count the number of rectangles. The product of 6 × 3 = 18.

3. The related fact for 6 × 3 = 18 is 3 × 6 = 18.

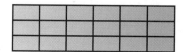

   Count the number of rectangles. The product of 3 and 6 is equal to the product of 6 and 3, which is 18.

YOUR TURN!

Draw an array to model 7 × 2. Then write and model the related multiplication fact.

1. Identify the first factor. _____

2. Identify the second factor. _____

   The product of 7 × 2 is _____.

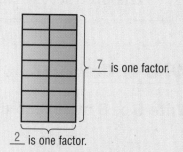

   _7_ is one factor.

   _2_ is one factor.

3. The related fact for 7 × 2 = 14 is _____ × _____ = _____.

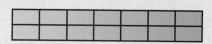

   The product of 7 and 2 is equal to the product of _____ and _____, which is _____.

Example 2

Use a number line to model 2 × 3.

1. Identify the first factor. **2**
   This is the number of times the group is repeated.

2. Identify the second factor. **3**
   This is the group size.

3. Draw a number line. Mark 2 groups of 3.

   The product is 6.

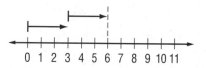

0 1 2 3 4 5 6 7 8 9 10 11

Copyright © by The McGraw-Hill Companies, Inc.

GO ON

YOUR TURN!

Use a number line to model 3 × 5.

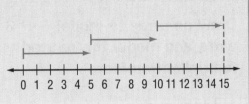

1. Identify the first factor. _____
2. Identify the second factor. _____
3. Draw a number line. Mark _____ groups of _____.

 The product is _____.

Who is Correct?

Write 5 × 8 as repeated addition.

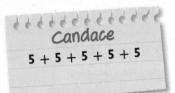

Candace

$5 + 5 + 5 + 5 + 5$

Juan

$5 + 5 + 5 + 5$
$+ 5 + 5 + 5 + 5$

Rose

$8 + 8 + 8 + 8 + 8$

Circle correct answer(s). Cross out incorrect answer(s).

 Guided Practice

Draw an array to model each multiplication fact. Then write and model each related multiplication fact.

1 5 × 3 _____

2 3 × 4 _____

  **Step by Step Practice**

3 Write 2 + 2 + 2 + 2 as a multiplication fact.

 Step 1 Identify the number being repeated. _____

 Step 2 Count how many times the number is repeated. _____

 Step 3 Write the multiplication fact.

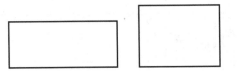

 _____ × _____

 how many times it is repeated   the number being repeated

Copyright © by The McGraw-Hill Companies, Inc.

Write each repeated addition fact as a multiplication fact.
Then write the related multiplication fact.

4 5 + 5 + 5 _____

5 4 + 4 + 4 + 4 + 4 _____

6 3 + 3 + 3 + 3 _____

Step by Step Problem-Solving Practice

Solve.

7 **INTERIOR DESIGN** Natalie's mom is tiling a rectangular floor. Each tile is 1 foot by 1 foot. The room is 8 feet by 10 feet. How many tiles will cover the floor?

Problem-Solving Strategies
☑ Draw a diagram.
☐ Use logical reasoning.
☐ Solve a simpler problem.
☐ Work backward.
☐ Use an equation.

Understand Read the problem. Write what you know.

The rectangular floor is _____ by

_____. Each tile is a _____ square.

Plan Pick a strategy. One strategy is to draw a diagram.

Solve Draw a rectangle. Divide the rectangle so it has 8 rows and 10 columns.

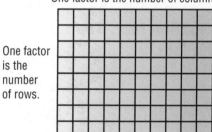

One factor is the number of columns.

One factor is the number of rows.

Write a multiplication fact for the array.

_____ × _____

Write the expression as repeated addition.

_____

_____

How many tiles will Natalie's mom need? _____

Check Count the squares in the diagram to check your answer.

GO ON

Copyright © by The McGraw-Hill Companies, Inc.

8 HEALTH Lakeesha takes one vitamin C tablet each morning. She takes one vitamin C tablet each night. Write a multiplication fact to show how many tablets Lakeesha needs for a 30-day supply. How many tablets is this? Check off each step.

_____ **Understand: I circled key words.**

_____ **Plan: To solve the problem, I will** _____.

_____ **Solve: The answer is** _____.

_____ **Check: I checked my answer by** _____.

9 MUSIC Mike's music teacher teaches each grade two times a week. If there are three grades, how many times does the music teacher teach each week? Write a multiplication fact to show how you found the answer.

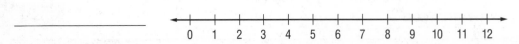

10 Reflect Use graph paper. Draw as many different arrays for the number 12 as possible.

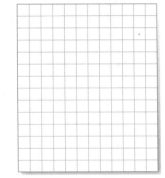

▶ **Skills, Concepts, and Problem Solving**

Use a number line to model each multiplication fact. Then write and model the related multiplication fact.

11 2 × 4

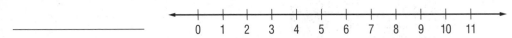

12 3 × 4

Copyright © by The McGraw-Hill Companies, Inc.

Draw an array to model each multiplication fact. Then write and model each related multiplication fact.

13 4 × 5 _____

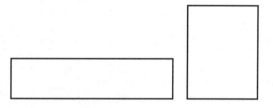

14 5 × 3 _____

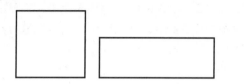

15 3 × 7 _____

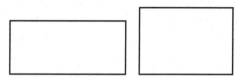

16 8 × 5 _____

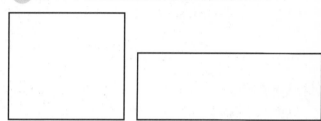

Write the multiplication fact as repeated addition. Then write the related multiplication fact. Find the product.

17 3 × 6 _____

_____

18 7 × 4 _____

_____

19 8 × 3 _____

_____

20 6 × 5 _____

_____

21 3 × 9 _____

_____

22 4 × 8 _____

_____

Write each repeated addition fact as a multiplication fact. Then write the related multiplication fact. Find the products.

23 11 + 11 + 11 _____

_____

24 2 + 2 + 2 + 2 + 2 _____

_____

25 5 + 5 + 5 + 5 _____

26 4 + 4 + 4 + 4 _____

_____

Copyright © by The McGraw-Hill Companies, Inc.

GO ON

Solve.

27 PACKAGING   There are two different packages of dinner rolls. One package has 8 rolls across and 2 rolls down. The other package has 3 rolls across and 4 rolls down. Which package has more rolls? How many more?

_____

28 STORAGE   Mr. Ramirez is buying a storage rack for art paper. One rack has 5 bins across and 3 bins down. Another rack has 2 bins across and 9 bins down. Which rack has more bins? How many more?

_____

29 CRAFTS   Gloria is making a puzzle from tiles. Her sheet of tiles is 10 inches by 9 inches. Each tile is 1-inch square. How many puzzle pieces of tile can she use in her pattern? Write an addition sentence to find the answer.

_____

Vocabulary Check   **Write the vocabulary word that completes each sentence.**

30 What operation is used to find the product of two numbers? _____

31 A(n) _____ is an arrangement of objects or symbols in rows of the same length and columns of the same length.

32 The numbers being multiplied are called _____.

33 Writing in Math   How can you show that 2 × 3 is equal to 3 × 2?

_____

_____

_____

STOP

Copyright © by The McGraw-Hill Companies, Inc.

Multiply with 0, 1, and 10

KEY Concept

The **Zero Property of Multiplication** states that any number multiplied by zero equals zero.

$5 \times 0 = 0$ because *five groups of zero equals zero.*

The **Identity Property of Multiplication** states that any number multiplied by one is equal to the other number.

$5 \times 1 = 5$ because *five groups of one equals five.*

When you multiply by 10, you can place a 0 in the place value to the right of the other factor.

Multiples of 10

$1 \times 10 = 10$	$6 \times 10 = 60$
$2 \times 10 = 20$	$7 \times 10 = 70$
$3 \times 10 = 30$	$8 \times 10 = 80$
$4 \times 10 = 40$	$9 \times 10 = 90$
$5 \times 10 = 50$	$10 \times 10 = 100$

VOCABULARY

Identity Property of Multiplication
if you multiply a number by one, the product is the same as the given number
Example: $8 \times 1 = 8$

Zero Property of Multiplication
if you multiply a number by zero, the product is zero
Example: $0 \times 5 = 0$

Example 1

Find 8×0

1. One of the factors is 0. So, you can use the Zero Property of Multiplication.

2. You know that the Zero Property of Multiplication states that any number times zero equals zero.

   $1 \times 0 = 0$

   $2 \times 0 = 0$

   $3 \times 0 = 0$

3. So, $8 \times 0 = 0$.

YOUR TURN!

Find 0×4

1. One of the factors is _____. So, you can use the _____.

2. You know that the _____ Property of Multiplication states that any number times _____.

   $0 \times 1 = $ _____

   $0 \times 2 = $ _____

   $0 \times 3 = $ _____

3. So, $0 \times 4 = $ _____.

GO ON

Copyright © by The McGraw-Hill Companies, Inc.

Example 2

Find 1 × 6

1. One of the factors is 1. So, you can use the Identity Property of Multiplication.

2. You know that the Identity Property of Multiplication states that any number multiplied by one is equal to the other number.

$$1 \times 1 = 1 \qquad 1 \times 4 = 4$$
$$1 \times 2 = 2 \qquad 1 \times 5 = 5$$
$$1 \times 3 = 3 \qquad 1 \times 6 = 6$$

3. So, $1 \times 6 = 6$.

YOUR TURN!

Find 5 × 1

1. One of the factors is ____. So, you can use the _____.

2. You know that the _____ Property of Multiplication states that any number _____ _____.

$$1 \times 1 = \underline{\quad} \qquad 4 \times 1 = \underline{\quad}$$
$$2 \times 1 = \underline{\quad} \qquad 5 \times 1 = \underline{\quad}$$
$$3 \times 1 = \underline{\quad}$$

3. So, $5 \times 1 = \underline{\quad}$.

Example 3

> To find the multiples of 10 you can skip count by 10.
> 10, 20, 30, 40, 50, 60, 70, 80, 90, 100

Find 7 × 10

1. One of the factors is 10.

2. Use skip counting by tens to help you find the answer.

   10, 20, 30, 40, 50, 60, 70, 80, 90, 100

3. The seventh term is 70.

4. The product 7×10 is 70.

YOUR TURN!

Find 10 × 3

1. One of the factors is ____.

2. Use skip counting by ____ to help you find the answer.

   ____, ____, ____, ____, ____, ____, ____, ____, ____, ____

3. The third term is ____.

4. The product _____ is ____.

Who is Correct?

Find the product of 12 and 1.

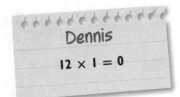
Dennis
12 × 1 = 0

Rafael
12 × 1 = 1

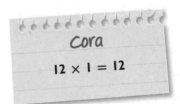
Cora
12 × 1 = 12

Circle correct answer(s). Cross out incorrect answer(s).

Copyright © by The McGraw-Hill Companies, Inc.

Guided Practice

Find each product. Name the property that you used to find the product.

1 7×1 _____

2 1×4 _____

3 0×1 _____

4 1×10 _____

5 3×0 _____

Step by Step Practice

6 Find 10×5.

    Step 1 One of the factors is ____.

    Step 2 Use skip counting by ____ to help find the answer.

    ____, ____, ____, ____, ____, ____, ____, ____, ____, ____

    Step 3 The ____ term is ____.

    Step 4 The product of 10×5 is ____.

Find each product.

7 $5 \times 0 =$ _____

8 $10 \times 1 =$ _____

9 $8 \times 10 =$ _____

10 $1 \times 0 =$ _____

11 $9 \times 1 =$ _____

12 $4 \times 10 =$ _____

13 $10 \times 10 =$ _____

14 $11 \times 1 =$ _____

15 $1 \times 7 =$ _____

16 $0 \times 11 =$ _____

Copyright © by The McGraw-Hill Companies, Inc.

GO ON

Find each product.

17 $7 \times 1 = $ _____

18 $4 \times 1 = $ _____

19 $8 \times 0 = $ _____

20 $10 \times 5 = $ _____

21 $0 \times 3 = $ _____

22 $3 \times 10 = $ _____

23 $10 \times 9 = $ _____

24 $0 \times 9 = $ _____

Step by Step Problem-Solving Practice

Solve.

25 FASHION   Emma plans to buy shirts that are on sale for $10 each. She wants to know how much money she will need to buy 2, 3, or 4 shirts. What is the price of 2, 3, and 4 shirts?

Problem-Solving Strategies

☐ Draw a diagram.
☐ Use logical reasoning.
☐ Solve a simpler problem.
☐ Work backward.
☑ Look for a pattern.

Understand   Read the problem. Write what you know.

Emma wants to buy shirts that are _____ each.

Plan   Pick a strategy. One strategy is to look for a pattern.

Solve   List the multiples of 10.

$1 \times 10 = $ _____
$2 \times 10 = $ _____
$3 \times 10 = $ _____

Look for the pattern. Notice that the ones digit of the product is _____, while the tens digit is _____.

Find the pattern.

What is the price of 2 shirts? _____
What is the price of 3 shirts? _____
What is the price of 4 shirts? _____

Check   Look over your answer. Did you answer the question?

Copyright © by The McGraw-Hill Companies, Inc.

26 NATURE   Adela planted a vine that grows 10 inches a month. How many inches will it grow in 6 months? Check off each step.

_____ Understand: I circled key words.

_____ Plan: To solve the problem, I will _____.

_____ Solve: The answer is _____.

_____ Check: I checked my answer by _____.

27 COMMUNITY SERVICE   Ms. Salter's class collected 7 bags of canned goods to donate to a food bank. If each bag held 10 cans, how many cans did they collect in all?

_____

28 Reflect   Explain why $76 \times 1 = 76$.

_____

_____

_____

_____

▶ **Skills, Concepts, and Problem Solving**

Find each product. Name the property that you used to find the product.

29 2×1 _____

30 1×5 _____

31 1×0 _____

32 1×11 _____

Copyright © by The McGraw-Hill Companies, Inc.

GO ON

Find each product.

33 $6 \times 0 =$ _____

35 $5 \times 10 =$ _____

37 $8 \times 1 =$ _____

39 $10 \times 6 =$ _____

41 $3 \times 1 =$ _____

43 $0 \times 10 =$ _____

45 $1 \times 12 =$ _____

34 $10 \times 4 =$ _____

36 $4 \times 0 =$ _____

38 $2 \times 10 =$ _____

40 $9 \times 1 =$ _____

42 $0 \times 6 =$ _____

44 $6 \times 1 =$ _____

46 $0 \times 12 =$ _____

Solve.

47 **FOOD** Hot dogs are packaged in groups of 10. How many hot dogs are in 5 packages?

_____

48 **MONEY** Ten pennies are equal to 1 dime. How many pennies are equal to 6 dimes?

_____

49 **POSTCARDS** Nick is on vacation in Egypt. He wants to send 1 postcard to each member of his family in the United States. Nick has 9 family members in the United States. How many postcards should he buy? Write the multiplication fact that helped you find the answer.

_____

FOOD Hot dogs are packaged in groups of 10.

Vocabulary Check **Write the vocabulary word that completes each sentence.**

50 The _____ states that when you multiply a number by one, the product is the same as the given number.

51 The property that states that when you multiply a number by zero, the product equals zero is called the

_____.

Copyright © by The McGraw-Hill Companies, Inc.

52 Writing in Math Find the missing number from the
number sentence. Explain your reasoning.

$$17 \times \boxed{} = 0$$

_____

_____

 Spiral Review

**Use a number line to model each multiplication fact. Then
write and model the related multiplication fact.** (Lesson 2-1, p. 58)

53 5×2

_____
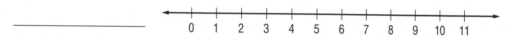

_____

54 6×3

_____

_____

55 SAFETY   Briscoe Bakery has an alarm system to keep the
building safe. The key pad on the alarm at Briscoe Bakery
has 4 keys across and 5 keys down. How many keys are on
the key pad? Write an addition sentence to find the answer.

_____

Copyright © by The McGraw-Hill Companies, Inc.

STOP

Use a number line to model each multiplication fact. Then write and model the related multiplication fact.

1 $2 \times 3 = 6$ _____

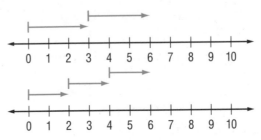

Draw an array to model the multiplication fact. Then write the related multiplication fact.

2 $3 \times 8 = 24$ _____

Write each repeated addition fact as a multiplication fact. Then write the related multiplication fact.

3 $9 + 9 + 9 + 9 + 9 + 9 + 9 =$ _____

4 $2 + 2 + 2 + 2 =$ _____

5 $1 + 1 + 1 + 1 + 1 =$ _____

Find each product.

6 $10 \times 4 =$ _____ **7** $12 \times 1 =$ _____ **8** $0 \times 9 =$ _____ **9** $6 \times 1 =$ _____

10 $1 \times 3 =$ _____ **11** $10 \times 2 =$ _____ **12** $0 \times 7 =$ _____ **13** $7 \times 10 =$ _____

Solve.

14 GAMES How many 1×1 squares are on the checkerboard shown? _____

15 COOKING To make one pizza, Tyrone uses 10 ounces of mushrooms, 8 ounces of pepperoni, 5 ounces of pizza sauce, and 4 ounces of cheese. How much of each ingredient will Tyrone need to make two pizzas?

_____

_____

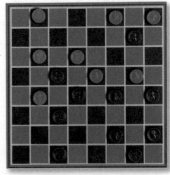

GAMES Checkerboards have 8 rows and 8 columns.

Copyright © by The McGraw-Hill Companies, Inc.

Multiply by 2

KEY Concept

Multiplying by 2 is another way to write the **double** facts for addition.

$2 + 2 = 4$	$3 + 3 = 6$	$4 + 4 = 8$	$5 + 5 = 10$
$6 + 6 = 12$	$7 + 7 = 14$	$8 + 8 = 16$	$9 + 9 = 18$

$10 + 10 = 20$

Multiples of 2 are the numbers you say when you skip count by 2s.

2, 4, 6, 8, 10, 12, 14, 16, 18, 20

There are several ways to say you are multiplying 9 by 2.
- the product of two and nine
- two times nine
- double the number nine
- twice the number nine

VOCABULARY

double or twice
two times a number; words that indicate to multiply by two are double a number or twice a number

multiple
a multiple of a number is the *product* of that number and any whole number
Example: 30 is a multiple of 10 because $3 \times 10 = 30$.

You should practice memorizing the multiplication facts of 2. The product is the same whether the factor 2 is the first factor or the second factor.

Example 1

Find the product of 8 and 2 by using repeated addition. Then write the two related multiplication facts.

1. What is the first factor? **8**
   What is the second factor? **2**

2. Write the product of 8 and 2 as repeated addition. You can use 2 as the number being added and the other factor as the number of times you add the number.
   $2 + 2 + 2 + 2 + 2 + 2 + 2 + 2 = 16$

3. Write the related multiplication facts.
   $8 \times 2 = 16$ $2 \times 8 = 16$

GO ON

Copyright © by The McGraw-Hill Companies, Inc.

YOUR TURN!

**Find the product of 5 and 2 by using repeated addition.
Then write two related multiplication facts.**

1. What is the first factor? _____ What is the second factor? _____

2. Write the product of 5 and 2 as repeated addition. You can use _____ as the number being added and the other factor as the number of times you add the number.

   _____

3. Write the related multiplication facts. _____ × _____ = _____

   _____ × _____ = _____

Example 2

Use an array to find the missing number.

$4 \times \boxed{} = 8$

1. How many rectangles should be inside the array? **8**

2. The factor already shown is 4. The array will have 4 rows.

3. Divide into columns until there are 8 rectangles in the array. The number of columns is the missing number. How many columns do you make? **2**

2 columns of 4 rows make 8 rectangles

4. The missing number is 2.
   4 × 2 = 8

YOUR TURN!

Use an array to find the missing number.

$6 \times \boxed{} = 12$

1. How many rectangles should be inside the array? _____

2. The factor already shown is _____. The array will have _____ rows.

3. Divide into columns until there are _____ rectangles. How many columns do you make? _____

_____ columns of _____ rows make _____ rectangles

4. The missing number is _____.
   6 × _____ = 12

Copyright © by The McGraw-Hill Companies, Inc.

Who is Correct?

Find the product of 12 and 2 using repeated addition.

Amber
12
+ 12
24

Peter
12
+ 2
14

Gigi
2
+ 2
4

Circle correct answer(s). Cross out incorrect answer(s).

 Guided Practice

Find each product by using repeated addition.

1 5 × 2 _____

2 9 × 2 _____

3 2 × 4 _____

4 2 × 10 _____

5 2 × 8 _____

6 2 × 2 _____

**Draw an array to model each fact. Find the product.
Then write the related multiplication fact.**

7 2 × 8 = _____

8 2 × 10 = _____

Step by Step Practice

Use an array to find the missing number.

9 2 × ⬚ = 12

Step 1 How many rectangles should be inside the array? _____

Step 2 The array will have _____ rows.

Step 3 Divide into columns until there are 12 rectangles.
How many columns do you use? _____

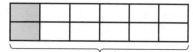

_____ columns of _____ rows make _____ rectangles

Step 4 2 × ⬚ = 12

GO ON

Copyright © by The McGraw-Hill Companies, Inc.

Use an array to find the missing number.

10 $2 \times \boxed{} = 18$

Build the array with _____ rows and a total of _____ squares. How many columns are there? _____

11 $2 \times \boxed{} = 6$

12 $2 \times \boxed{} = 10$

13 $2 \times \boxed{} = 14$

14 $2 \times \boxed{} = 8$

Step by Step Problem-Solving Practice

Solve.

15 Each game token at Arny's Arcade costs $2. Irina wants to buy 9 tokens. How much money does she need?

Problem-Solving Strategies
☑ Draw a diagram.
☐ Use logical reasoning.
☐ Solve a simpler problem.
☐ Work backward.
☐ Look for a pattern.

Understand Read the problem. Write what you know.

Game tokens cost _____. Irina wants to buy _____ tokens.

Plan Pick a strategy. One strategy is to draw a diagram.

Solve Draw an array that has _____ rows and _____ columns.

Count the number of smaller rectangles.

The cost of 9 game tokens is _____.

Check You can skip count by 2s nine times.

Copyright © by The McGraw-Hill Companies, Inc.

16 **GAMES**   Marjorie and Helen have one bag of 18 marbles. They each take a marble from the bag until the bag is empty. How many marbles does each girl get? Check off each step.

_____ Understand: I circled key words.

_____ Plan: To solve the problem, I will _____.

_____ Solve: The answer is _____.

_____ Check: I checked my answer by _____.

17 **BOOKS**   Over the summer, two students each read 7 books. How many books did they read total? _____

18 **Reflect**   How do you use repeated addition to multiply by 2?

_____

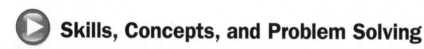

Skills, Concepts, and Problem Solving

Find each product by using repeated addition.

19 2×8 _____

20 6×2 _____

21 2×0 _____

22 1×2 _____

Use an array to find the missing number.

23 $2 \times \boxed{} = 8$

24 $2 \times \boxed{} = 12$

25 $\boxed{} \times 2 = 14$

26 $\boxed{} \times 2 = 22$

GO ON

Copyright © by The McGraw-Hill Companies, Inc.

27 ☐ × 2 = 10 ▢

28 3 × ☐ = 6 ▢

Solve.

29 **PACKAGING** Paper towels come in packages of 2. How many rolls are there in 8 packages? _____

30 **MONEY** A dime is worth 2 nickels. If you have 5 dimes, how many nickels would have the same value?

_____

31 **FASHION** Kraig bought 3 pairs of shoes. How many shoes does he have? _____

Vocabulary Check **Write the vocabulary word that completes each sentence.**

32 In the expression 2 × 3, 2 and 3 are _____.

33 When you _____ a number, you multiply the number by 2.

34 **Writing in Math** Use words to say you are multiplying 2 by 4 in three different ways.

_____

_____

▶ Spiral Review

Find each product. Name the property that you used to find the product. (Lesson 2-2, p. 61)

35 0 × 11 _____

36 1 × 5 _____

Solve. (Lesson 2-1, p. 54)

37 **BOOKS** Valerie has 36 books to put on 4 shelves. The same number of books will be placed on each shelf. How many books will be on each shelf? _____

STOP

Copyright © by The McGraw-Hill Companies, Inc.

Multiply by 5

KEY Concept

Multiples of 5 are the numbers you say when you skip count by 5.

5, 10, 15, 20, 25, 30, 35, 40, 45, 50

Consider the **fact family** with 4, 5, and 20.

$5 \times 4 = 20$ ← related multiplication facts → $4 \times 5 = 20$

$20 \div 5 = 4$ ← related division facts → $20 \div 4 = 5$

You should practice memorizing the multiplication facts of 5. The product is the same whether the **factor** 5 is the first factor or the second factor.

VOCABULARY

fact family
a group of related facts using the same numbers
Example: $5 \times 3 = 15$,
$3 \times 5 = 15$,
$15 \div 5 = 3$,
$15 \div 3 = 5$

factor
a number that divides into a whole number evenly; also a number that is multiplied by another number

Example 1

Find the product of 5 and 7 by using repeated addition. Then write the two related multiplication facts.

1. What is the first factor? **5**
   What is the second factor? **7**

2. Write the product of 5 and 7 as repeated addition. Use 5 as the number being added. Use the other factor as the number of times you add the number.
   $5 + 5 + 5 + 5 + 5 + 5 + 5 = 35$

3. Write the related multiplication facts.
   $5 \times 7 = 35$
   $7 \times 5 = 35$

YOUR TURN!

Find the product of 9 and 5 by using repeated addition. Then write the two related multiplication facts.

1. What is the first factor? _____
   What is the second factor? _____

2. Write the product of 9 and 5 as repeated addition. Use _____ as the number being added. Use the other factor as the number of times you add the number.

   _____

   _____

3. Write the related multiplication facts.

   _____ × _____ = _____
   _____ × _____ = _____

GO ON

Copyright © by The McGraw-Hill Companies, Inc.

Example 2

Skip count to find the missing number.

$$5 \times \boxed{} = 30$$

1. One of the factors is 5.

2. Use skip counting by 5s to help you find the answer.

   5, 10, 15, 20, 25, 30, 35, 40, 45, 50

3. The sixth term is 30.

4. The multiplication fact is
   $5 \times 6 = 30$.

5. The missing number is 6.

YOUR TURN!

Skip count to find the missing number.

$$5 \times \boxed{} = 45$$

1. One of the factors is _____.

2. Use skip counting by _____ to help you find the answer.

   _____, _____, _____, _____, _____, _____,
   _____, _____, _____, _____

3. The _____ term is _____.

4. The multiplication fact is

   _____.

5. The missing number is _____.

Who is Correct?

Find the product of 5 and 6 by using repeated addition.

Charlie

$5 + 6 = 30$

Vito

$5 + 5 + 5 + 5 +$
$5 + 5 = 30$

Meli

$6 + 6 + 6 + 6$
$+ 6 = 30$

Circle correct answer(s). Cross out incorrect answer(s).

▶ Guided Practice

Find each product by using repeated addition.

1 $5 \times 5 =$ _____

2 $5 \times 9 =$ _____

_____   _____

Copyright © by The McGraw-Hill Companies, Inc.

3 $5 \times 4 =$ _____

4 $1 \times 5 =$ _____

5 $3 \times 5 =$ _____

_____

6 $8 \times 5 =$ _____

_____

7 $2 \times 5 =$ _____

8 $0 \times 5 =$ _____

9 $10 \times 5 =$ _____

_____

10 $5 \times 6 =$ _____

_____

Step by Step Practice

11 **Skip count to find the missing number.**

$5 \times \boxed{} = 35$

Step 1 One of the factors is _____.

Step 2 Use skip counting by _____ to help you find the answer.

_____, _____, _____, _____, _____, _____, _____, _____, _____, _____

Step 3 The _____ term is _____.

Step 4 The product of _____ is _____.

Step 5 The missing number is _____.

Copyright © by The McGraw-Hill Companies, Inc.

GO ON

Skip count to find the missing number.

12 ☐ × 5 = 40

_____ , _____ , _____ , _____ , _____ , _____ , _____ , _____ , _____ , _____

The product of _____ is _____ .

The missing number is _____ .

13 ☐ × 5 = 5

14 5 × ☐ = 20

15 ☐ × 5 = 25

16 5 × ☐ = 55

17 ☐ × 5 = 50

18 5 × ☐ = 60

19 ☐ × 5 = 15

20 5 × ☐ = 40

Step by Step Problem-Solving Practice

Problem-Solving Strategies
☑ Draw a diagram.
☐ Use logical reasoning.
☐ Solve a simpler problem.
☐ Work backward.
☐ Look for a pattern.

Solve.

21 **PARKS** There are 5 benches in the park. Each bench has 3 children sitting on it. How many children are sitting on the benches altogether?

Understand Read the problem. Write what you know.
There are _____ benches.
_____ children are on each bench.

Plan Pick a strategy. One strategy is to draw a picture. Read the problem. Draw a rectangle for each bench. Draw a circle for each child.

Solve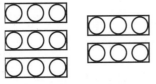

number of benches × number of children on each bench = total children
_____   ×   _____   =   _____ .

Check Count the circles in the picture. Does the count match your answer?

Copyright © by The McGraw-Hill Companies, Inc.

22 **BUSINESS**   An after-school club is going on a field trip. Parents with vans have offered to drive the students. If there are 25 students in the club, how many vans will be needed if each van holds 5 students? Check off each step.

_____ Understand: I circled key words.

_____ Plan: To solve the problem, I will _____.

_____ Solve: The answer is _____.

_____ Check: I checked my answer by _____.

23 **PACKAGING**   Each box holds 5 markers. Jamira has 3 boxes. How many markers does she have?

_____

24 **Reflect**   Write the multiples of 5 up to 50. What is the pattern of the numbers in the ones place?

_____

_____

▶ Skills, Concepts, and Problem Solving

Find each product by using repeated addition.

25 5×1 _____

_____

26 6×5 _____

_____

27 5×10 _____

_____

28 0×5 _____

_____

GO ON

Copyright © by The McGraw-Hill Companies, Inc.

Skip count to find the missing number.

29 $\boxed{} \times 5 = 0$

30 $5 \times \boxed{} = 5$

31 $\boxed{} \times 5 = 60$

32 $5 \times \boxed{} = 50$

33 $\boxed{} \times 5 = 45$

34 $5 \times \boxed{} = 10$

35 $\boxed{} \times 5 = 35$

36 $5 \times \boxed{} = 15$

Solve.

37 **MUSIC** Marcus's albums have 5 songs on each side. There are 2 sides. If Marcus has 5 albums, how many songs do they contain in all?

_____

MUSIC Marcus collects vinyl albums.

38 **LANDSCAPING** Alice plans to plant flowers and place them in 5 rows. She wants 5 flowers in each row. How many flowers will Alice plant in all?

_____

39 **DVDS** Trevor wants to purchase DVDs of his favorite TV show. Each DVD has 5 episodes of the show. There are 4 different DVDs. How many episodes will Trevor buy?

_____

40 **VACATION** Mr. Malone works for a bookstore. He earns 5 hours of vacation each month. He has worked for the bookstore for 3 months. Suppose that he has not used any of his vacation. How many hours of vacation has he earned?

_____

Vocabulary Check **Write the vocabulary word that completes each sentence.**

41 An example of a _____ for the numbers 5, 12, and 60 is $5 \times 12 = 60$; $12 \times 5 = 60$; $60 \div 5 = 12$; and $60 \div 12 = 5$.

42 A number that is multiplied by another number is a(n) _____.

Copyright © by The McGraw-Hill Companies, Inc.

43 Writing in Math Draw a picture of seating 30 students in 5 rows. How many seats in each row? Show and explain how this is related to multiplication.

_____

_____

 Spiral Review

Solve. (Lesson 2-3, p. 69)

44 SCHOOL SUPPLIES Jack has 8 pencils in his desk. Ramona has twice as many pencils as Jack. How many pencils does Ramona have? Write a multiplication sentence to explain your answer.

_____

45 FASHION Rita bought 7 pairs of socks. How many new socks does she have? Write a multiplication sentence to explain your answer.

_____

Find each product. (Lesson 2-2, p. 61)

46 8 × 10 _____   **47** 9 × 1 _____   **48** 0 × 12 _____

Draw an array to model 4 × 3. Then write and model each related multiplication fact. (Lesson 2-1, p. 54)

49 4 × 3 _____

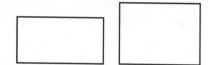

Copyright © by The McGraw-Hill Companies, Inc.

STOP

Draw an array to model each multiplication fact. Find the product. Then write a related multiplication fact.

1 $2 \times 9 =$ _____

2 $3 \times 5 =$ _____

Find each product by using repeated addition.

3 3×2 _____

4 4×5 _____

5 9×1 _____

6 10×0 _____

Find each product.

7 5×9 _____

8 7×2 _____

9 0×5 _____

10 1×2 _____

11 8×5 _____

12 2×5 _____

13 6×2 _____

14 5×6 _____

Skip count to find the missing number.

15 $\boxed{} \times 5 = 45$

16 $5 \times \boxed{} = 30$

Solve.

17 **MONEY** Five nickels have the same value as 1 quarter. How many nickels have the same value as 7 quarters?

18 **HOBBIES** Hakeem collects salt-and-pepper shaker sets. If each set consists of 1 salt shaker and 1 pepper shaker, how many shakers does he have if he has 8 sets?

Copyright © by The McGraw-Hill Companies, Inc.

Multiply by 3

KEY Concept

Multiples of 3 are the numbers you say when you skip count by 3s.

3, 6, 9, 12, 15, 18, 21, 24, 27, 30

Triple is a word that means to *multiply by three*. There are several ways to say you are multiplying 6 by 3.

- the **product** of three and six
- three times six
- three multiplied by six
- triple the number six

You should practice memorizing the multiplication facts of 3. The product is the same whether the **factor** 3 is the first factor or the second factor.

VOCABULARY

factor
a number that divides into a whole number evenly; also a number that is multiplied by another number
Example: $3 \times 4 = 12$
factors

product
the answer or result of a multiplication problem; it also refers to expressing a number as the product of its factors
Example: $3 \times 4 = \underbrace{12}_{product}$

triple
a number that is multiplied by 3, or added together 3 times
Example: "triple 2" is $3 \times 2 = 6$

Example 1

Find the product of 3 and 9 by using repeated addition. Then write the two related multiplication facts.

1. What is the first factor? **3**
   What is the second factor? **9**

2. Write a number sentence as repeated addition. You can use 3 as the number being added and the other factor as the number of times you add the number.
   $3 + 3 + 3 + 3 + 3 + 3 + 3 + 3 + 3 = 27$

3. Write the related multiplication facts.
   $3 \times 9 = 27$
   $9 \times 3 = 27$

Copyright © by The McGraw-Hill Companies, Inc.

GO ON

Copyright © by The McGraw-Hill Companies, Inc.

YOUR TURN!

Find the product of 3 and 4 by using repeated addition.
Then write the two related multiplication facts.

1. What is the first factor? _____
   What is the second factor? _____

2. Write an equation as repeated addition. You can use _____
   as the number being added and the other factor as the
   number of times you add the number.

   _____

3. Write the related multiplication facts.   _____ × _____ = _____
                                              _____ × _____ = _____

Example 2

Use an array to find the missing number.

$3 \times \boxed{} = 18$

1. The factor already in the equation is 3. The array will have 3 rows.

2. Continue making columns until there are 18 rectangles. How many columns do you make? **6**

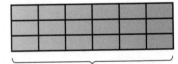

6 columns of 3 rows make 18 rectangles

3. The missing number is 6.
   The completed fact is $3 \times 6 = 18$.

YOUR TURN!

Use an array to find the missing number.

$3 \times \boxed{} = 15$

1. The factor already in the equation is _____. The array will have _____ rows.

2. Continue making columns until there are 15 rectangles. How many columns do you make? _____

_____ columns of _____ rows make _____ rectangles

3. The missing number is _____.
   The completed fact is
   _____ × _____ = _____.

Who is Correct?

Find the missing number.   3 × _____ = 33

Ethan
3 × 11 = 33

Heather
3 × 10 = 33

Shawanna
3 × 1 = 33

Circle correct answer(s). Cross out incorrect answer(s).

 ## Guided Practice

Find each product.

1 9 × 3 _____

2 5 × 3 _____

3 3 × 4 _____

4 3 × 3 _____

**Draw an array to model each fact. Find the product.
Then write its related multiplication fact.**

5 3 × 8 = _____

6 3 × 10 = _____

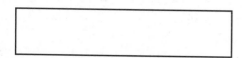

7 Find the product of 2 and 3 using repeated addition.
Then write the two related multiplication facts.

Step 1 What is the first factor? _____
What is the second factor? _____

Step 2 Write a number sentence as repeated addition.
You can use 3 as the number being added. Use
the other factor as the number of times you add
the number.

_____

Step 3 Write the related multiplication facts.

_____

GO ON

Copyright © by The McGraw-Hill Companies, Inc.

Find each product by using repeated addition.

8 $3 \times 3 = \boxed{} + \boxed{} + \boxed{} = $ _____

9 $3 \times 4 = \boxed{} + \boxed{} + \boxed{} + \boxed{} = $ _____

10 $3 \times 7 = $ _____

11 $1 \times 3 = $ _____

_____

12 $3 \times 8 = $ _____

13 $10 \times 3 = $ _____

_____

14 $3 \times 0 = $ _____

15 $5 \times 3 = $ _____

Step by Step Problem-Solving Practice

Problem-Solving Strategies
- ☑ Draw a diagram.
- ☐ Use logical reasoning.
- ☐ Solve a simpler problem.
- ☐ Work backward.
- ☐ Look for a pattern.

Solve.

16 **TRAVEL**   Three minivans were used for a family reunion trip. Each van will seat 8 people. How many people can go in the minivans?

Understand   Read the problem. Write what you know.
There are _____ minivans.
Each van will seat _____ people.

Plan   Pick a strategy. One strategy is to draw a diagram.

Solve   You can make an array to show the number of seats on minivans. The array will have _____ rows and _____ columns.

Count the number of rectangles in the array.

How many people can go in the minivans?

_____

Check   Use repeated addition to check your answer.

Copyright © by The McGraw-Hill Companies, Inc.

17 INDUSTRY A factory that makes tennis balls puts 3 balls in each can. If a case has 24 tennis balls, how many cans are there in each case?
Check off each step.

_____ Understand: I circled key words.

_____ Plan: To solve the problem, I will _____.

_____ Solve: The answer is _____.

_____ Check: I checked my answer by _____.

18 SHOPPING Joe had to make 3 round trips to the market. The market is 4 miles from his house. How many miles did Joe travel to make the 3 round trips? _____

19 Reflect Write a multiplication fact for each phrase below. Find the product of each multiplication fact.

nine times three _____

the product of three and two _____

three multiplied by zero _____

triple the number one _____

 Skills, Concepts, and Problem Solving

Find each product by using repeated addition.

20 $3 \times 5 =$ _____

21 $3 \times 3 =$ _____

22 $3 \times 1 =$ _____

23 $0 \times 3 =$ _____

Use an array to find the missing number.

24 $3 \times \boxed{} = 9$

25 $3 \times \boxed{} = 30$

26 $3 \times \boxed{} = 12$

27 $3 \times \boxed{} = 21$

GO ON

Copyright © by The McGraw-Hill Companies, Inc.

Find each product by using repeated addition.

28 7×3 _____

29 3×6 _____

30 10×3 _____

31 3×9 _____

Solve.

32 CONSTRUCTION   Zane is building a square rabbit crate. He needs to have 3 boards for each side. How many boards will he need? _____

33 TENNIS   After her tennis lesson, Alisha is putting tennis balls back into their cans. If each can holds 3 tennis balls, how many cans will she use to hold 27 balls? _____

34 NUTRITION   Ti watches his diet carefully to make sure he eats 3 pieces of fruit each day. How many pieces of fruit does he eat in 1 week? _____

Vocabulary Check   **Write the vocabulary word that completes each sentence.**

35 The answer in a multiplication problem is the _____.

36 When you multiply a number by 3, you _____ it.

37 Writing in Math   Harry was asked to triple the number nine. He wrote $9 + 3 = 12$. What did Harry do wrong?

_____

_____

 Spiral Review

Solve. (Lesson 2-4, p. 75)

38 INTERIOR DESIGN   A door in Darnell's home has 3 columns of window panes. How many rows are there if there are 15 panes total? _____

Write the multiplication fact as repeated addition. Then write the related multiplication fact. Find the product. (Lesson 2-1, p. 54)

39 3×7 _____

40 9×4 _____

_____

_____

STOP

Copyright © by The McGraw-Hill Companies, Inc.

Vocabulary and Concept Check

array, *p. 54*

fact family, *p. 75*

factor, *p. 54*

Identity Property of Multiplication, *p. 61*

multiple, *p. 69*

product, *p. 54*

Zero Property of Multiplication, *p. 61*

Write the vocabulary word that completes each sentence.

1 An arrangement of objects in rows of the same length and columns of the same length are in a(n)

_____.

2 The related facts $3 \times 2 = 6$, $2 \times 3 = 6$, $6 \div 3 = 2$, and $6 \div 2 = 3$ are all part of the same

_____.

3 The _____ states that any number times zero equals zero.

4 A(n) _____ of a number is the product of that number and any whole number.

Lesson Review

2-1 Introduction to Multiplication (pp. 54–60)

Draw an array to model 2 × 3. Then write and model the related multiplication fact.

5 _____

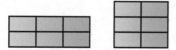

Write each multiplication fact as repeated addition. Then write the related multiplication facts.

6 4 × 5 _____

_____

7 7 × 3 _____

_____

Example 1

Find the product of 4 and 2 using repeated addition. Then write two related multiplication facts.

1. What is the first factor? **4**

   What is the second factor? **2**

2. Write a number sentence as repeated addition. Use the first factor as the number being added. Use the second factor as the number of times you add the number. **4 + 4 = 8**

3. Write one multiplication fact.
   4 × 2 = 8

4. Write the related multiplication fact.
   2 × 4 = 8

Copyright © by The McGraw-Hill Companies, Inc.

2-2 Multiply with 0, 1, and 10 (pp. 61–67)

Find each product. Name the property that you used to find the product.

8 0 × 9 _____

_____

9 1 × 3 _____

_____

Find each product.

10 8 × 0 _____

11 6 × 1 _____

12 10 × 9 _____

13 0 × 10 _____

Example 2

Find 0 × 4.

1. One of the factors is 0.
   So, you can use the Zero Property of Multiplication.

2. You know that the Zero Property of Multiplication states that any number times zero equals zero.

3. So, 0 × 4 = 0.

2-3 Multiply by 2 (pp. 69–74)

Find each product using repeated addition.

14 2 × 4 _____

15 8 × 2 _____

16 2 × 1 _____

Use an array to find the missing number.

17 2 × ⬚ = 8

⬚

18 5 × ⬚ = 10

⬚

Example 3

Find the product of 3 and 2 using repeated addition. Then write two related multiplication facts.

1. What is the first factor? **3**
   What is the second factor? **2**

2. Write a number sentence as repeated addition. Use the first factor as the number being added. Use the second factor as the number of times you add the number. **3 + 3 = 6**

3. Write one multiplication fact.
   3 × 2 = 6

4. Write the related multiplication fact.
   2 × 3 = 6

Copyright © by The McGraw-Hill Companies, Inc.

2-4 Multiply by 5 (pp. 75–81)

Find each product by using repeated addition.

19 5×4 _____

20 2×5 _____

21 5×6 _____

Skip count to find the missing number.

22 $5 \times \boxed{} = 35$

23 $\boxed{} \times 9 = 45$

24 $\boxed{} \times 5 = 0$

Example 4

Skip count to find the missing number.

$$5 \times \boxed{} = 15$$

1. Use skip counting by 5s to help you find the answer.

2. The third term is 15.

3. The product of 5×3 is 15.

4. The missing number is 3.

2-5 Multiply by 3 (pp. 83–88)

Find each product using repeated addition.

25 3×4

_____

26 8×3

_____

27 7×3

_____

Use an array to find the missing number.

28 $1 \times \boxed{} = 3$

$\boxed{}$

Example 5

Find the product of 3 and 6 by using repeated addition. Then write the two related multiplication facts.

1. What is the first factor? **3**
   What is the second factor? **6**

2. Write an equation as repeated addition. Use the first factor as the number being added. Use the second factor as the number of times you add the number.
   $3 + 3 + 3 + 3 + 3 + 3 = 18$

3. Write the multiplication fact.
   $3 \times 6 = 18$

4. Write the related multiplication fact.
   $6 \times 3 = 18$

Copyright © by The McGraw-Hill Companies, Inc.

Chapter Test

Draw an array to model each fact. Then write the related multiplication fact.

1 2×3

_____

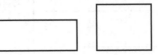

2 1×5

_____

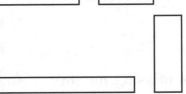

Use a number line to model each multiplication fact. Then write and model the related multiplication fact.

3 3×2

_____

_____

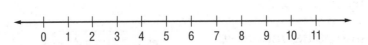

Find each product by using repeated addition.

4 6×3 _____

5 2×7 _____

_____

_____

Find each product.

6 8×0 _____

7 1×12 _____

8 3×10 _____

9 0×1 _____

10 7×2 _____

11 11×3 _____

12 3×8 _____

13 5×6 _____

14 8×5 _____

15 6×6 _____

16 12×3 _____

17 9×2 _____

GO ON

Copyright © by The McGraw-Hill Companies, Inc.

Draw an array to model and find each product.

18 3×9 _____

[ ]

19 5×11 _____

[ ]

Find the missing number.

20 $5 \times \boxed{} = 45$ 　　　　　　**21** $3 \times \boxed{} = 18$

Solve.

22 MUSIC   Neva has 5 shelves in her CD stand. Each shelf holds 12 CDs. What is the greatest number of CDs that Neva's stand will hold?

_____

23 MOVING   When Sunde moved to a new apartment, he packed his belongings into his truck. To make the move, he had to make 3 trips. Each trip was 12 miles long. How many miles did he drive during the move?

_____

Correct the mistakes.

24 Carly told Selena that she knew a shortcut for multiplying by 10. She said, "You add two zeros to the other factor." Selena told her that shortcut was not right. What was Carly's mistake?

_____

_____

_____

Copyright © by The McGraw-Hill Companies, Inc.

STOP

Choose the best answer and fill in the corresponding circle on the sheet at right.

1 Which answer choice has the same value as $1 + 1 + 1 + 1 + 1 + 1$?

A $2 + 3 + 4 + 5$ **C** $10 - 5$

B 1×6 **D** 6×2

2 Which answer choice shows 5×7 as repeated addition?

A $5 + 7$

C $5 + 5 + 5 + 5 + 5 + 5 + 5$

B $5 + 5 + 5$ **D** 7×5

3 Alita eats a hot lunch 5 days a month. Her friend Olivia eats a hot lunch twice as often each month. Which math sentence shows how many hot lunches Olivia eats per month?

A $2 \times 6 = 12$ **C** $2 \times 2 = 4$

B $5 + 2 = 7$ **D** $5 \times 2 = 10$

4 Find the product.

$$10 \times 7$$

A 70   **C** 7

B 17   **D** 700

5 A bag of potatoes is on sale for $3. If Lu buys 7 bags, how much does he spend on potatoes?

A $4   **C** $18

B $10   **D** $21

6 Priya is baking cookies. She makes 10 small cookies in each batch. If she bakes 5 batches, how many cookies does she make?

A 5 cookies   **C** 50 cookies

B 15 cookies   **D** 55 cookies

7 Which numbers multiply to give a product of 18?

A 5×3 **C** 9×2

B 18×0 **D** 6×4

8 Curtis reads 3 chapters of his book each day. How many chapters does Curtis read in a week (7 days)?

A 10   **C** 28

B 21   **D** 35

9 Each bottle of juice costs $2 at the market. Felipe has $6. How many bottles of juice can he buy?

A 1   **C** 4

B 3   **D** 0

GO ON

Copyright © by The McGraw-Hill Companies, Inc.

10 Alonso is placing 90 books onto book-shelves. He would like to place 10 books on each shelf. How many shelves will he need?

A 2   C 5

B 9   D 10

---

11 On Saturday, Nayla ate 8 strawberries. On Sunday, she ate twice as many strawberries. How many strawberries did she eat on Sunday?

A 4   C 8

B 24   D 16

---

12 Kiera bought two of the same item. She spent exactly $14. Which item did she buy?

A socks

B book

C T-shirt

D CD

Copyright © by The McGraw-Hill Companies, Inc.

ANSWER SHEET

Directions: Fill in the circle of each correct answer.

1   Ⓐ Ⓑ Ⓒ Ⓓ
2   Ⓐ Ⓑ Ⓒ Ⓓ
3   Ⓐ Ⓑ Ⓒ Ⓓ
4   Ⓐ Ⓑ Ⓒ Ⓓ
5   Ⓐ Ⓑ Ⓒ Ⓓ
6   Ⓐ Ⓑ Ⓒ Ⓓ
7   Ⓐ Ⓑ Ⓒ Ⓓ
8   Ⓐ Ⓑ Ⓒ Ⓓ
9   Ⓐ Ⓑ Ⓒ Ⓓ
10   Ⓐ Ⓑ Ⓒ Ⓓ
11   Ⓐ Ⓑ Ⓒ Ⓓ
12   Ⓐ Ⓑ Ⓒ Ⓓ

Success Strategy

Read each problem carefully and look at each answer choice. Eliminate answers you know are wrong. This narrows your choices even before solving the problem.

STOP

More Multiplication

You can use multiplication to decide how much money you will earn.

Pilar is helping her mother make dinner. Her mother has agreed to give Pilar $4 for each meal she helps prepare. Pilar plans to help her mother for 6 meals. How much money will she earn?

STEP **2** Preview   Get ready for Chapter 3. Review these skills and compare them with what you will learn in this chapter.

What You Know	What You Will Learn
You know that changing the order in which you multiply smaller numbers does not change the product. $2 \times 3 = 6$ $3 \times 2 = 6$	*Lessons 3-1 through 3-5* $7 \times 9 = 63$ $9 \times 7 = 63$ Changing the order in which you multiply greater numbers does not change the product.
You know how to make an array. **Example:** 	*Lessons 3-1 through 3-5* You can use an array to find a missing factor in a multiplication fact. $5 \times \boxed{} = 10$ The array has 5 rows. It has a total of 10 rectangles. $5 \times 2 = 10$

You know how to add greater numbers.
 	
Examples: $14 + 14 = 28$
           $18 + 18 = 36$
 	
TRY IT!
 	
1 $14 + 7 = $ _____
 	
2 $32 + 16 = $ _____
 	
3 $18 + 18 + 9 = $ _____
	Lessons 3-1 through 3-5
	
	Multiplication is repeated addition. The sums of greater numbers can be grouped to help you add them more easily.
	
	$4 \times 7 = \underbrace{7 + 7} + \underbrace{7 + 7} = 28$
	        14 $+$ 14 $= 28$
	
	$4 \times 9 = \underbrace{9 + 9} + \underbrace{9 + 9} = 36$
	        18 $+$ 18 $= 36$

Multiply by 4

KEY Concept

Multiples of 4 are the numbers you say when you skip count by 4.

4, 8, 12, 16, 20, 24, 28, 32, 36, 40

Consider the **fact family** with 4, 7, and 28.

$4 \times 7 = 28 \leftarrow$ related multiplication facts $\rightarrow 7 \times 4 = 28$

$28 \div 4 = 7 \leftarrow$ related division facts $\rightarrow 28 \div 7 = 4$

You can model multiplication with an **array**.

4×5 is 4 groups of 5, or, 4 rows and 5 columns.

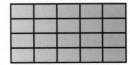

The **product** is the total number of rectangles in the array.

The product is the same whether 4 is the first factor or the second factor.

VOCABULARY

array
an arrangement of objects or symbols in rows of the same length and columns of the same length; the length of a row might be different from the length of a column

fact family
a group of related facts using the same numbers

multiple
a multiple of a number is the *product* of that number and any whole number

product
the answer or result of a multiplication problem; it also refers to expressing a number as the product of its factors

Example 1

Draw an array to model 4 × 8. Find the product. Then write the related multiplication facts.

1. The first factor is 4, so there will be 4 rows. The second factor is 8, so there will be 8 columns.

2. Label the array 4 × 8. Count the number of rectangles. **32**

3. Write two related multiplication facts. **4 × 8 = 32**
   8 × 4 = 32

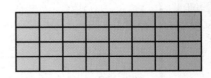

4 × 8

Copyright © by The McGraw-Hill Companies, Inc.

YOUR TURN!

Draw an array to model 4 × 7. Find the product. Then write the related multiplication facts.

1. The first factor is a _____, so there will be _____ rows. The second factor is a _____, so there will be _____ columns.

2. Label the array. Count the number of rectangles.

   _____

   _____ × _____

3. Write two related multiplication facts.

   _____ × _____ = _____

   _____ × _____ = _____

Example 2

Find the product of 4 and 8 by skip counting.

$4 \times 8 = \boxed{}$

1. One of the factors is 4.

2. Use skip counting by 4s to help you find the answer.

   4, 8, 12, 16, 20, 24, 28, 32, 36, 40,…

3. The 8th term is 32.

4. 4 × 8 = 32

YOUR TURN!

Find the product of 3 and 4 by skip counting.

$3 \times 4 = \boxed{}$

1. One of the factors is _____.

2. Use skip counting by _____ to help you find the answer.

   _____, _____, _____, _____, _____,

   _____, _____, _____, _____, _____,…

3. The _____ term is _____.

4. 3 × 4 = _____

Who is Correct?

Find the product of 5 and 4 by skip counting.

Ciara

5, 10, 15, 20, 25, …

5 × 4 = 25

Jordan

4, 8, 12, 14, 16, …

5 × 4 = 16

Reno

4, 8, 12, 16, 20, …

5 × 4 = 20

Circle correct answer(s). Cross out incorrect answer(s).

GO ON

Copyright © by The McGraw-Hill Companies, Inc.

▶ Guided Practice

Draw an array to model each multiplication fact. Find the product. Then write the related multiplication facts.

1 $2 \times 4 =$ _____

_____

2 $6 \times 4 =$ _____

_____

Find each product.

3 $5 \times 4 =$ _____

4 $4 \times 10 =$ _____

5 $3 \times 4 =$ _____

6 $2 \times 4 =$ _____

7 $8 \times 4 =$ _____

8 $6 \times 4 =$ _____

9 $1 \times 4 =$ _____

10 $4 \times 4 =$ _____

11 $4 \times 9 =$ _____

Step by Step Practice

Use an array to find the missing number.

12 $4 \times \boxed{} = 36$

Step 1 The factor shown is _____.

The array will have _____ rows.

Step 2 Make columns until there are 36 rectangles. How many columns do you make? _____

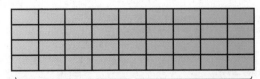

_____ columns of 4 rows make 36 rectangles.

Step 3 $4 \times \boxed{} = 36$

Copyright © by The McGraw-Hill Companies, Inc.

**Draw an array to model each multiplication fact.
Then use the array to find the missing number.**

13 $4 = 4 \times \boxed{}$

number of rows: _____

total number of rectangles: _____

number of columns: _____

14 $4 \times \boxed{} = 20$

15 $16 = 4 \times \boxed{}$

Step by Step Problem-Solving Practice

Solve.

16 **FARMING** There are 4 pumpkins on each vine in Ms. Cotter's garden. She wants to bring one pumpkin to each of the 25 students in her class. She has 7 vines in her garden. Will she have enough pumpkins for her class?

Understand	Read the problem. Write what you know.

_____ pumpkins grow on each vine.

There are _____ vines.

There are _____ students.

Plan Pick a strategy. One strategy is to draw a picture.

Solve There are 7 vines, and each vine holds 4 pumpkins.

ᗝ-ᗝ-ᗝ-ᗝ ᗝ-ᗝ-ᗝ-ᗝ ᗝ-ᗝ-ᗝ-ᗝ ᗝ-ᗝ-ᗝ-ᗝ
ᗝ-ᗝ-ᗝ-ᗝ ᗝ-ᗝ-ᗝ-ᗝ ᗝ-ᗝ-ᗝ-ᗝ

number of pumpkins × number of vines = total number of pumpkins

_____ × _____ = _____

Are there enough pumpkins? _____

Check Count the pumpkins to check your answer.

Problem-Solving Strategies

☑ Draw a picture.

☐ Use logical reasoning.

☐ Solve a simpler problem.

☐ Work backward.

☐ Use an equation.

Copyright © by The McGraw-Hill Companies, Inc.

GO ON

17 **FASHION** A shoe store is having a sale. If Percy buys
4 pairs of shoes, how many shoes will he take home in all?

Check off each step.

_____ Understand: I circled key words.

_____ Plan: To solve the problem, I will _____.

_____ Solve: The answer is _____.

_____ Check: I checked my answer by _____.

18 **GAMES** Joanne needs tokens to play a videogame.
For every dollar she puts in the machine, she gets 2 tokens.
If she puts $4 into the machine, how many tokens will she get?

_____

19 **Reflect** Write the fact family for 4, 6, and 24.

_____

 Skills, Concepts, and Problem Solving

**Draw an array to model each multiplication fact. Find the
product. Then write the related multiplication facts.**

20 $4 \times 1 =$ _____

_____

21 $5 \times 4 =$ _____

_____

22 $4 \times 7 =$ _____

_____

23 $4 \times 8 =$ _____

_____

Copyright © by The McGraw-Hill Companies, Inc.

Find each product.

24 $0 \times 4 =$ _____

25 $4 \times 5 =$ _____

26 $10 \times 4 =$ _____

27 $7 \times 4 =$ _____

28 $4 \times 4 =$ _____

29 $9 \times 4 =$ _____

30 $11 \times 4 =$ _____

31 $4 \times 8 =$ _____

32 $4 \times 6 =$ _____

Draw an array to model each multiplication fact. Then use the array to find the missing number.

33 $4 \times \boxed{} = 16$

34 $4 \times \boxed{} = 8$

35 $4 \times \boxed{} = 40$

36 $4 \times \boxed{} = 4$

37 $4 \times \boxed{} = 12$

38 $24 = 4 \times \boxed{}$

39 $20 = 4 \times \boxed{}$

40 $4 \times \boxed{} = 28$

41 $32 = 4 \times \boxed{}$

42 $4 \times \boxed{} = 36$

Copyright © by The McGraw-Hill Companies, Inc.

GO ON

Solve.

43 PACKAGING   There are 24 students in Mr. Wells's class. He buys 6 boxes of markers, so he can give one marker to each student. How many markers are in each box? Write the multiplication fact that helped you find the answer.

_____

44 SOCCER   Aja has soccer practice each day after school. If the soccer team practices for 4 weeks, how many times will she go to practice? Write the multiplication fact that helped you find the answer.

_____

45 SCHOOL   Mrs. Palmer's classroom has 9 rows of seats. There are 4 seats in each row. How many seats are there in her classroom? Write the multiplication fact that helped you find the answer.

_____

46 FOOD   Louis bought small packs of crackers for his snack. Each package has 10 crackers. If he ate 4 packs of crackers, how many crackers did he eat? Write the multiplication fact that helped you find the answer.

_____

Vocabulary Check   Write the vocabulary word that completes each sentence.

47 A group of related facts using the same numbers is a(n) _____.

48 A _____ of a number is the product of that number and any whole number.

49 Writing in Math   Name two ways you can find the multiples of 4.

_____

_____

Copyright © by The McGraw-Hill Companies, Inc.

STOP

Multiply by 6

KEY Concept

Multiples of 6 are the numbers you say when you skip count by 6.

6, 12, 18, 24, 30, 36, 42, 48, 54, 60

Consider the **fact family** with 6, 8, and 48.
$6 \times 8 = 48$ ← related multiplication facts → $8 \times 6 = 48$
$48 \div 6 = 8$ ←   related division facts   → $48 \div 8 = 6$

Practice memorizing the multiplication facts of 6. The product is the same whether the factor 6 is the first factor or the second factor.

VOCABULARY

fact family
a group of related facts using the same numbers

multiple
a multiple of a number is the *product* of that number and any whole number
Example: 30 is a multiple of 10 because $3 \times 10 = 30$

Example 1

Draw an array to model 6 × 7. Find the product. Then write the related multiplication facts.

1. The first factor is 6, so there will be 6 rows. The second factor is 7, so there will be 7 columns.

6×7

2. Label the array 6×7.
   Count the number of rectangles. **42**

3. Write two related multiplication facts.
   $6 \times 7 = 42$
   $7 \times 6 = 42$

YOUR TURN!

Draw an array to model 6 × 8. Find the product. Then write the related multiplication facts.

1. The first factor is _____, so there will be _____ rows.
   The second factor is _____, so there will be _____ columns.

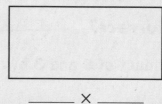
   _____ × _____

2. Label the array. Count the number of rectangles. _____

3. Write two related multiplication facts.

   _____ × _____ = _____

   _____ × _____ = _____

   GO ON

Copyright © by The McGraw-Hill Companies, Inc.

Example 2

Find the product of 6 and 7 by using repeated addition. Then write two related multiplication facts.

1. What is the first factor? **6**

2. What is the second factor? **7**

3. Write the product of 6 and 7 as repeated addition.

    It may help to group the numbers as you add them.

    $\underbrace{6 + 6}$ + $\underbrace{6 + 6}$ + $\underbrace{6 + 6}$ + 6 =

    $\underbrace{12 + 12}$ + $\underbrace{12 + 6}$ =

    24 + 18 = 42

4. Write one multiplication fact.

    6 × 7 = 42

5. Write the related multiplication fact.

    7 × 6 = 42

YOUR TURN!

Find the product of 6 and 5 by using repeated addition. Then write two related multiplication facts.

1. What is the first factor? _____

2. What is the second factor? _____

3. Write the product of 6 and 5 as repeated addition.

    Group the numbers as you add them.

    $\underbrace{\underline{} + \underline{}}$ + $\underbrace{\underline{} + \underline{}}$ + $\underline{}$ =

    $\underbrace{\underline{} + \underline{}}$ + $\underline{}$ =

    $\underline{}$ + $\underline{}$ = $\underline{}$

4. Write one multiplication fact.

    _____

5. Write the related multiplication fact.

    _____

Who is Correct?

Find the product of 6 and 3 by using repeated addition.

Shannon
6 + 6 + 6 =
12 + 6 = 18

Jeremy
3 + 3 + 3 + 3 + 3 =
6 + 6 + 3 = 15

Vita
6 + 6 + 6 =
12 + 3 = 15

Circle correct answer(s). Cross out incorrect answer(s).

Copyright © by The McGraw-Hill Companies, Inc.

Copyright © by The McGraw-Hill Companies, Inc.

Guided Practice

Draw an array to model each multiplication fact. Find the product. Then write the related multiplication facts.

1 $1 \times 6 =$ ___

2 $6 \times 4 =$ ___

Find each product by using repeated addition.

3 $6 \times 6 =$ _____

4 $0 \times 6 =$ _____

5 $3 \times 6 =$ _____

6 $6 \times 8 =$ _____

Step by Step Practice

7 Find the missing number by using repeated addition.

$$6 \times \boxed{} = 30$$

Step 1 One factor is _____.

Step 2 Use repeated addition.

$6 + 6 =$ ___ $+ 6 =$ ___ $+ 6 =$ ___ $+ 6 =$ ___

Step 3 How many times do you add 6 to find 30? _____

Step 4 $6 \times \boxed{} = 30$

8 Find the missing number by using repeated addition.

$$6 \times \boxed{} = 18$$

$6 + 6 =$ ___ $+ 6 =$ ___

The missing number is _____.

GO ON

Find each missing number by using repeated addition.

9 $6 \times \boxed{} = 42$

$6 + 6 =$ ___ $+ 6 =$ ___ $+ 6 =$ ___ $+ 6 =$ ___ $+ 6 =$ ___ $+ 6 =$ ___

10 $6 \times \boxed{} = 24$

11 $6 \times \boxed{} = 54$

12 $6 \times \boxed{} = 0$

Step (by) Step Problem-Solving Practice

Problem-Solving Strategies
- ☐ Draw a diagram.
- ☑ Use logical reasoning.
- ☐ Solve a simpler problem.
- ☐ Work backward.
- ☐ Guess and check.

13 **CELEBRATIONS**   Violet invited 6 people to her birthday party. She bought 2 bags filled with toy prizes. Each bag had 24 prizes. She gave each person at the party the same number of prizes. How many prizes did each person receive?

Understand   Read the problem. Write what you know.

There are _____ bags of toy prizes.

Each bag has _____ prizes.

There are _____ people at the party.

Plan   Pick a strategy. One strategy is to use logical reasoning.

Solve   How can you find the total number of prizes in each bag? Multiply the number of bags times the number of prizes in each bag.

_____ × _____ = _____

There are _____ total prizes.

How can you find the number of prizes for each person?

number for each person × each person = total prizes

_____ × _____ = _____

Each person will receive _____ prizes.

Check   You can act it out using small cubes or pieces of paper.

Copyright © by The McGraw-Hill Companies, Inc.

14 **SURVEYS**   Karl asked people leaving a movie theater how well they liked the movie. He stopped every sixth person. If Karl stopped 9 people, how many people walked by him in all?

Check off each step.

_____ Understand: I circled key words.

_____ Plan: To solve the problem, I will _____.

_____ Solve: The answer is _____.

_____ Check: I checked my answer by _____.

15 **COMMUNITY SERVICE**   Olinda collected canned goods to donate to a food bank. Every house she visited gave her 6 cans of food. If she has 36 cans of food, how many houses did she visit? _____

16 **Reflect**   Bob is planting 12 seeds in a garden. He wants to plant the same number of seeds in each row. Draw arrays to show the different ways that Bob could plant the seeds.

 Skills, Concepts, and Problem Solving

Draw an array to model each multiplication fact. Find the product. Then write the related multiplication facts.

17 $6 \times 2 =$ _____

18 $6 \times 5 =$ _____

_____

_____

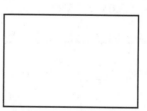

Find each product by using repeated addition.

19 $6 \times 7 =$ _____

20 $1 \times 6 =$ _____

21 $6 \times 3 =$ _____

22 $9 \times 6 =$ _____

GO ON

Copyright © by The McGraw-Hill Companies, Inc.

Solve.

23 **HOBBIES**   Zion sews baby quilts. He wants to double the size of each quilt. The small quilts are made from 30 squares. How many squares will the larger quilts need? _____

The larger quilts have 6 squares in each row. How many squares will be in each column? _____

24 **CALENDAR**   Marisol is making a calendar for the month of January. She will draw 6 rows for the number of weeks. She will draw 7 columns for the number of days. How many boxes will she draw in all? _____

January has 31 days. She will write a number in 31 boxes. How many boxes will not have a number? _____

Vocabulary Check   **Write the vocabulary word that completes each sentence.**

25 The answer to a multiplication problem is the _____.

26 A(n) _____ of a number is the product of that number and any whole number.

27 **Writing in Math**   Brad is writing related multiplication facts. He wrote 6 × 9 = 54 and 6 × 9 = 54. What did he do wrong?

_____

_____

▶ Spiral Review

Find each product. (Lesson 3-1, p. 98)

28 10 × 4 = _____

29 4 × 6 = _____

Solve.

30 **SCRAPBOOK**   Devin is adding 4 pages to his scrapbook. He will place 8 photos on each page. How many photos will Devin add to his scrapbook?

_____

Copyright © by The McGraw-Hill Companies, Inc.

STOP

Multiply by 7

KEY Concept

Multiples of 7 are the numbers you say when you skip count by 7.

7, 14, 21, 28, 35, 42, 49, 56, 63, 70

Practice memorizing the multiplication facts of 7. The factor 7 can be the first factor or the second factor.

VOCABULARY

multiple
a multiple of a number is the *product* of that number and any whole number
Example: 30 is a multiple of 10 because 3 × 10 = 30

Example 1

Draw an array to model 7 × 3. Find the product. Then write the related multiplication facts.

1. The first factor is 7, so there will be 7 rows.
   The second factor is 3, so there will be 3 columns.

2. Label the array 7 × 3. Count the number of rectangles. 21

3. Write the related multiplication facts. 7 × 3 = 21
                                            3 × 7 = 21

7 × 3

YOUR TURN!

Draw an array to model 7 × 6. Find the product. Then write the related multiplication facts.

1. The first factor is _____, so there will be _____ rows.

   The second factor is _____, so there will be _____ columns.

2. Label the array _____ × _____. Count the number of rectangles. _____

3. Write the related multiplication facts.

   _____ × _____ = _____

   _____ × _____ = _____

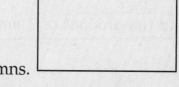

_____ × _____

GO ON

Copyright © by The McGraw-Hill Companies, Inc.

Example 2

Find the product of 7 and 8 by using repeated addition. Then write two related multiplication facts.

1. What is the first factor? **7**

2. What is the second factor? **8**

3. Write the product of 7 and 8 as repeated addition.

   It may help to group the numbers as you add them.

   $7 + 7 + 7 + 7 + 7 + 7 + 7 + 7 =$

   $14 + 14 + 14 + 14 =$

   $28 + 28 = 56$

4. Write one multiplication fact.
   $7 \times 8 = 56$

5. Write the related multiplication fact.
   $8 \times 7 = 56$

Copyright © by The McGraw-Hill Companies, Inc.

YOUR TURN!

Find the product of 7 and 4 by using repeated addition. Then write two related multiplication facts.

1. What is the first factor? _____

2. What is the second factor? _____

3. Write the product of 7 and 4 as repeated addition. Group the numbers as you add them.

   _____ + _____ + _____ + _____ =

   _____ + _____ = _____

4. Write one multiplication fact.

   _____

5. Write the related multiplication fact.

   _____

Who is Correct?

Find the product of 7 and 5 by using repeated addition.

Val
$5 + 5 + 5 + 5 + 5 =$
$10 + 10 + 5 =$
$20 + 5 =$
25

Shaq
$7 + 7 + 7 + 7 + 7 =$
$14 + 14 + 7 =$
$14 + 21 =$
35

Helena
$5 + 5 + 5 + 5 + 5 + 5 =$
$10 + 10 + 10 =$
$20 + 10 =$
30

Circle correct answer(s). Cross out incorrect answer(s).

▶ Guided Practice

Draw an array to model each multiplication fact. Find the product. Then write the related multiplication facts.

1 $8 \times 7 = $ ___

2 $7 \times 2 = $ ___

Step by Step Practice

3 Find the missing number by using repeated addition.

$$7 \times \boxed{} = 49$$

Step 1 One factor is _____.

Step 2 Use repeated addition.

$7 + 7 = $ ___ $+ 7 = $ ___ $+ 7 = $ ___ $+ 7 = $ ___ $+ 7 = $ ___ $+ 7 = $ ___

Step 3 How many times do you add 7 to find 49? _____

Step 4 $7 \times \boxed{} = 49$

Find each product by using repeated addition.

4 $4 \times 7 = $ _____

5 $7 \times 5 = $ _____

6 $8 \times 7 = $ _____

7 $10 \times 7 = $ _____

8 $7 \times 6 = $ _____

9 $7 \times 3 = $ _____

10 $0 \times 7 = $ _____

11 $7 \times 2 = $ _____

GO ON ▶

Copyright © by The McGraw-Hill Companies, Inc.

Step by Step Problem-Solving Practice

Solve.

Problem-Solving Strategies
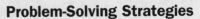
☑ Draw a picture.
☐ Use logical reasoning.
☐ Solve a simpler problem.
☐ Work backward.
☐ Act it out.

12 **MUSIC**   A harp is a stringed musical instrument with 7 pedals. A music room has 9 harps. How many harp pedals are there in the room?

Understand   Read the problem. Write what you know.

Each harp has _____ pedals.

There are _____ harps.

Plan   Pick a strategy. One strategy is to draw a picture.

Solve   Draw 9 figures to show 9 harps. On each figure, place a 7 to show the pedals.

Use repeated addition to find the number of pedals.

$7 + 7 + 7 + 7 + 7 + 7 + 7 + 7 + 7 =$ _____

There are _____ pedals.

Check   Does the answer make sense? Look over your solution. Did you answer the question?

13 **NATURE**   Rico planted 6 trees along his back fence. Each tree has 7 branches. How many total branches are on the trees?

Check off each step.

_____ Understand: I circled key words.

_____ Plan: To solve the problem, I will _____.

_____ Solve: The answer is _____.

_____ Check: I checked my answer by _____.

Copyright © by The McGraw-Hill Companies, Inc.

14 **ENTERTAINMENT**   At a dinner party, there are 8 round tables that seat 7 people each. There were 60 people at the party. Will there be enough seats? Explain.

_____

15 Reflect   Are the multiplication facts 4 × 3 and 6 × 2 related multiplication facts? Explain your answer.

_____

_____

 Skills, Concepts, and Problem Solving

Draw an array to model each multiplication fact. Find the product. Then write the related multiplication facts.

16 7 × 3 = _____

17 7 × 5 = _____

_____   _____

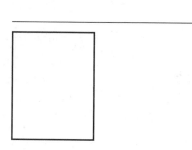   

Use an array to find each missing number.

18 7 × [ ] = 14

19 7 × [ ] = 63

20 7 × [ ] = 35

21 7 × [ ] = 49

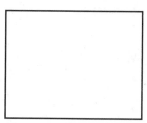   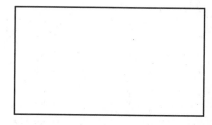

Copyright © by The McGraw-Hill Companies, Inc.

GO ON

Find each product.

22 7 × 7 = _____

23 7 × 8 = _____

24 7 × 3 = _____

25 7 × 1 = _____

26 7 × 5 = _____

27 7 × 4 = _____

28 9 × 7 = _____

29 6 × 7 = _____

Solve.

30 **SCIENCE**   A sea urchin grew 2 centimeters each year. How many centimeters did it grow in 7 years if it grew the same amount each year?

_____

SCIENCE sea urchin

31 **BOOKS**   Sundra builds a bookcase with 7 shelves. Each shelf holds 9 books. What is the number of books that each bookshelf holds?

_____

32 **HIKING**   Jeff hikes an average of 4 miles per hour. He hikes for a total of 7 hours. How many miles will he have hiked?

_____

33 **CALENDAR**   A teacher is counting the number of days until summer vacation. There are 10 weeks left. There are 7 days in each week. How many days until summer vacation?

_____

Copyright © by The McGraw-Hill Companies, Inc.

Vocabulary Check   Write the vocabulary word that completes each sentence.

34 The order in which two _____ are multiplied does not change the product.

35 Forty is a(n) _____ of 10 because $4 \times 10 = 40$.

36 **Writing in Math**   Describe an everyday situation in which you would use multiplication.

_____

_____

_____

 **Spiral Review**

Solve. (Lesson 3-2, p. 105)

37 **BOOK CLUB**   Each week Paquito reads 3 books. How many books will Paquito have read after 6 weeks? Write the multiplication fact that helped you find the answer.

_____

38 **FOOD**   Mrs. Agosto's restaurant needs 36 eggs. The market sells 6 eggs in a carton. How many cartons of eggs should she buy? Write the multiplication fact that helped you find the answer.

_____

Draw an array to model each multiplication fact. Find the product. Then write the related multiplication facts. (Lesson 3-1, p. 98)

39 $4 \times 6 =$ _____

_____

40 $4 \times 9 =$ _____

_____

STOP

Copyright © by The McGraw-Hill Companies, Inc.

Draw an array to model each multiplication fact. Find the product. Then write the related multiplication facts.

1 $6 \times 7 =$ _____

2 $6 \times 4 =$ _____

_____

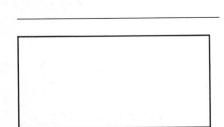

_____

Draw an array to model each multiplication fact. Then find the missing number that would make the equation true.

3 $7 \times \boxed{} = 28$

4 $6 \times \boxed{} = 54$

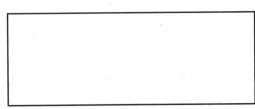

Find each product.

5 $0 \times 7 =$ _____

6 $6 \times 3 =$ _____

7 $6 \times 7 =$ _____

8 $6 \times 1 =$ _____

9 $7 \times 9 =$ _____

10 $8 \times 6 =$ _____

11 $7 \times 8 =$ _____

12 $5 \times 6 =$ _____

13 $6 \times 6 =$ _____

Solve.

14 **ENTERTAINMENT** The Hamilton family is having a reunion. They want seats for all 42 people. A table can seat 6. If tables rent for $7 each, how many tables will the family need to rent? How much will it cost to rent that many tables?

_____

15 **MACHINES** An engineer designed a machine to paint car parts. If the machine paints 60 parts an hour, how many parts does it paint in 10 minutes? (*Hint*: There are 60 minutes in one hour.)

_____

Copyright © by The McGraw-Hill Companies, Inc.

Copyright © by The McGraw-Hill Companies, Inc.

Lesson 3-4

Multiply by 8

KEY Concept

Multiples of 8 are the numbers you say when you skip count by 8.

8, 16, 24, 32, 40, 48, 56, 64, 72, 80

You should practice memorizing the multiplication facts of 8. The **product** is the same whether the **factor** 8 is the first factor or the second factor.

VOCABULARY

factor
a number that divides into a whole number evenly; also a number that is multiplied by another number

product
the answer or result of a multiplication problem; it also refers to expressing a number as the product of its factors

Example 1

Draw an array to model 8 × 5. Find the product. Then write the related multiplication facts.

1. The first factor is 8, so there will be 8 rows. The second factor is 5, so there will be 5 columns.

2. Label the array 8 × 5. Count the number of rectangles. **40**

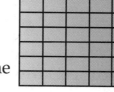

8 × 5

3. Write the related multiplication facts. **8 × 5 = 40**
   5 × 8 = 40

YOUR TURN!

Draw an array to model 8 × 3. Find the product. Then write the related multiplication facts.

1. The first factor is _____, so there will be _____ rows. The second factor is _____, so there will be _____ columns.

2. Label the array. Count the number of rectangles. _____

3. Write the related multiplication facts.

   ____ × ____ = ____

   ____ × ____ = ____

_____ × _____

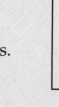

GO ON

Example 2

Find the missing number.

$8 \times \boxed{} = 32$

1. What number times 8 equals 32?
2. The missing number is 4.

   $8 \times 4 = 32$

YOUR TURN!

Find the missing number.

$8 \times \boxed{} = 64$

1. What number times _____ equals _____?
2. The missing number is _____.

   $8 \times \boxed{} = 64$

Who is Correct?

Find the missing number.

$8 \times \boxed{} = 48$

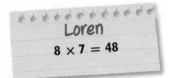
Loren
$8 \times 7 = 48$

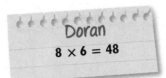
Doran
$8 \times 6 = 48$

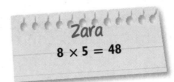
Zara
$8 \times 5 = 48$

Circle correct answer(s). Cross out incorrect answer(s).

▶ Guided Practice

Draw an array to model each multiplication fact. Find the product. Then write the related multiplication facts.

1 $8 \times 5 =$ _____

_____

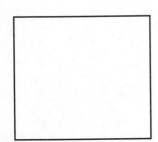

2 $8 \times 1 =$ _____

_____

Copyright © by The McGraw-Hill Companies, Inc.

Find each product.

3 $8 \times 8 =$ _____

4 $8 \times 6 =$ _____

5 $8 \times 5 =$ _____

6 $8 \times 10 =$ _____

7 $3 \times 8 =$ _____

8 $8 \times 9 =$ _____

9 $7 \times 8 =$ _____

10 $0 \times 8 =$ _____

Step by Step Practice

11 **Find the missing number.**

$8 \times \boxed{} = 24$

Step 1 What number times 8 is 24?

Step 2 The missing number is _____.

$8 \times \boxed{} = 24$

Find the missing number.

12 $8 \times \boxed{} = 40$

The array has

_____ rows

_____ columns

_____ rectangles

13 $8 \times \boxed{} = 16$

The array has

_____ rows

_____ columns

_____ rectangles

14 $8 \times \boxed{} = 48$

15 $3 \times \boxed{} = 24$

16 $9 \times \boxed{} = 72$

Copyright © by The McGraw-Hill Companies, Inc.

GO ON

Step by Step Problem-Solving Practice

Solve.

Problem-Solving Strategies

☐ Draw a diagram.
☐ Use logical reasoning.
☐ Solve a simpler problem.
☐ Work backward.
☑ Make a table.

17 **BUSINESS** A flower shop puts 8 flowers in each vase. If the shop sold 7 vases, how many flowers did it sell?

Understand Read the problem. Write what you know.

Each vase has _____ flowers.
The shop sold _____ vases.

Plan Pick a strategy. One strategy is to make a table.

Make a table with two columns. Title one column "vases" and the other "flowers."

Solve Complete the table. If 7 vases were sold, then _____ flowers were used.

Check Draw a picture and count the flowers to check your answer.

Vases	Flowers
1	8
2	16
3	
4	

18 **LANDSCAPING** A garden has 6 rows and 8 columns of flowers. How many flowers are in the garden?

Check off each step.

_____ Understand: I circled key words.

_____ Plan: To solve the problem, I will _____.

_____ Solve: The answer is _____.

_____ Check: I checked my answer by _____.

19 **BAKING** To make one batch of cookies, Toby needs 8 ounces of raisins and 7 ounces of oatmeal. He wants to triple the batch. How many ounces of raisins and oatmeal will he need?

Copyright © by The McGraw-Hill Companies, Inc.

20 [Reflect] Explain how to find the missing number for a multiplication fact. Give an example.

_____

_____

 ## Skills, Concepts, and Problem Solving

Draw an array to model each multiplication fact. Find the product. Then write the related multiplication facts.

21 $8 \times 7 =$ ____

22 $5 \times 8 =$ ____

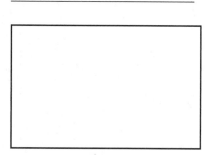

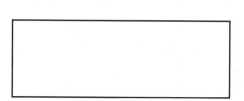

Find each product.

23 $8 \times 6 =$ _____

24 $1 \times 8 =$ _____

25 $9 \times 8 =$ _____

26 $8 \times 0 =$ _____

Find each missing number.

27 $8 \times \boxed{} = 16$

28 $8 \times \boxed{} = 64$

29 $8 \times \boxed{} = 40$

30 $8 \times \boxed{} = 56$

Solve.

31 EARTH SCIENCE   Niyna was collecting earthworms for science class. After 8 shovels of soil, she had found 40 worms. Each shovel of soil had the same number of worms. How many worms were in each shovel of soil?

_____

GO ON

Copyright © by The McGraw-Hill Companies, Inc.

Solve.

32 **HOBBIES** Jake collects baseball caps. He keeps them in boxes that hold 8 caps each. If there are 4 boxes, how many baseball caps does Jake have?

_____

Vocabulary Check **Write the vocabulary word that completes each sentence.**

33 The _____ is the answer to a multiplication problem.

34 In a(n) _____ the objects or symbols are arranged in rows of the same length and columns of the same length.

35 **Writing in Math** How is multiplication related to addition?

_____

_____

 Spiral Review

Find the missing number. (Lesson 3-3, p. 111)

36 $7 \times \boxed{} = 28$

The array has
_____ rows
_____ columns
_____ rectangles

37 $7 \times \boxed{} = 21$

The array has
_____ rows
_____ columns
_____ rectangles

Solve. (Lesson 3-2, p. 105)

38 **EXERCISE** Florence is training to run a marathon. She set the exercise machine to jog 6 miles each hour. She jogs for 3 hours. How many miles did she jog?

_____

39 **FOOTBALL** The Eastwood Eagles scored 7 touchdowns in the last football game. The team earns 6 points for each touchdown. How many points did they earn by scoring touchdowns?

_____

STOP

Copyright © by The McGraw-Hill Companies, Inc.

Lesson 3-5 Multiply by 9

KEY Concept

Multiples of 9 are the numbers you say when you skip count by 9.

9, 18, 27, 36, 45, 54, 63, 72, 81, 90

Notice the pattern in the products when multiplying a one-digit number by 9. The sum of the digits in the product is always equal to 9.

VOCABULARY

factor
a number that divides into a whole number evenly; also a number that is multiplied by another number

---

The product is the same whether the **factor** 9 is the first factor or the second factor.

Example 1

Draw an array to model 9 × 3. Find the product. Then write the related multiplication facts.

1. The first factor is 9, so there will be 9 rows. The second factor is 3, so there will be 3 columns.

2. Label the array 9 × 3. Count the number of rectangles. **27**

3. Write the related multiplication facts.
   9 × 3 = 27   3 × 9 = 27

9 × 3

> Building an array will work for any two factors. However, it is not always practical for large numbers.

YOUR TURN!

Draw an array to model 9 × 6. Find the product. Then write the related multiplication facts.

1. The first factor is _____, so there will be _____ rows. The second factor is _____, so there will be _____ columns.

2. Label the array _____ × _____. Count the number of rectangles. _____

3. Write the related multiplication facts.
   ____ × ____ = ____
   ____ × ____ = ____

_____ × _____

GO ON

Copyright © by The McGraw-Hill Companies, Inc.

Example 2

Find the product of 9 and 4 by using repeated addition.

1. What is the first factor? **9**

2. What is the second factor? **4**

3. Write the product of 9 and 4 as repeated addition.

   It may help to group the numbers as you add them.

   $9 + 9 + 9 + 9 =$

   $18 + 18 = 36$

4. Write the multiplication fact.

   $9 \times 4 = 36$

YOUR TURN!

Find the product of 9 and 5 by using repeated addition.

1. What is the first factor? _____

2. What is the second factor? _____

3. Write the product of 9 and 5 as repeated addition. Group the numbers as you add them.

   ___ + ___ + ___ + ___ + ___ =

   ___ + ___ + ___ =

   ___ + ___ = ___

4. Write the multiplication fact.

   _____

Example 3

Find the missing number.

$9 \times \boxed{} = 45$

1. Think about the multiplication facts. What number times 9 equals 45? **5**

   $9 \times 4 = 36 \qquad 9 \times 5 = 45$
   $9 \times 6 = 54 \qquad 9 \times 7 = 63$

2. $9 \times \boxed{} = 45$

YOUR TURN!

Find the missing number.

$9 \times \boxed{} = 63$

1. Think about the multiplication facts. What number times 9 equals 63?

   _____

   $9 \times 6 = \underline{} \qquad 9 \times 7 = \underline{}$
   $9 \times 8 = \underline{} \qquad 9 \times 9 = \underline{}$

2. $9 \times \boxed{} = 63$

Copyright © by The McGraw-Hill Companies, Inc.

Who is Correct?

Find the product of 9 and 4 using repeated addition.

Arturo
4 + 9 = 13

William
4 + 4 + 4 + 4 =
8 + 8 =
16

Koko
9 + 9 + 9 + 9 =
18 + 18 =
36

Circle correct answer(s). Cross out incorrect answer(s).

 Guided Practice

Draw an array to model each multiplication fact. Find the product. Then write the multiplication facts.

1 $9 \times 2 =$ ___

_____

2 $9 \times 4 =$ ___

_____

 **Step by Step Practice**

3 **Find the missing number.**

$9 \times \boxed{} = 72$

Step 1 Think about the multiplication facts.
What number times 9 equals ___?

$9 \times 6 =$ ___ $9 \times 7 =$ ___

$9 \times 8 =$ ___ $9 \times 9 =$ ___

Step 2 $9 \times \boxed{} = 72$

GO ON

Copyright © by The McGraw-Hill Companies, Inc.

Find the product by using repeated addition.

4 $9 \times 1 =$ _____

5 $9 \times 8 =$ _____

6 $9 \times 3 =$ _____

7 $9 \times 7 =$ _____

8 $9 \times 10 =$ _____

9 $6 \times 9 =$ _____

10 $9 \times 0 =$ _____

11 $9 \times 9 =$ _____

Step by Step Problem-Solving Practice

Solve.

12 **PACKAGING** At an open house, a teacher serves muffins and juice. The muffins are in packages of 10. The teacher buys 9 packages. How many muffins will the teacher have?

Problem-Solving Strategies	
☐ Draw a diagram.	
☐ Use logical reasoning.	
☑ Solve a simpler problem.	
☐ Work backward.	
☐ Make a table.	

Understand   Read the problem. Write what you know.

Each package contains _____ muffins.
There are _____ packages.

Plan   Pick a strategy. One strategy is to solve a simpler problem.

One of the factors is 9. To find the total number of muffins, you can skip count by 9s.

Solve   Skip count by 9s.

_____, _____, _____, _____, _____,
_____, _____, _____, _____, _____

The _____ term is _____.

_____

The teacher will have _____ muffins total.

Check   Draw a picture and count the muffins to check your answer.

Copyright © by The McGraw-Hill Companies, Inc.

13 **HOBBIES** Carla made 9 bracelets. There are 3 leather straps braided in each bracelet. How many straps did she use?

Check off each step.

_____ **Understand: I circled key words.**

_____ **Plan: To solve the problem, I will** _____.

_____ **Solve: The answer is** _____.

_____ **Check: I checked my answer by** _____.

14 **FLOWERS** Salvatore made bouquets of flowers. Each bouquet had 6 flowers. He made 9 bouquets. How many flowers did he use?

_____

15 **Reflect** Describe the pattern in the products when multiplying a one-digit number by 9.

_____

_____

 ## Skills, Concepts, and Problem Solving

Draw an array to model each multiplication fact. Find the product. Then write the related multiplication facts.

16 $9 \times 6 =$ ___

_____

17 $5 \times 9 =$ ___

_____

Copyright © by The McGraw-Hill Companies, Inc.

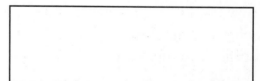

Find each product using repeated addition.

18 $9 \times 5 =$ _____

19 $2 \times 9 =$ _____

_____

_____

20 $9 \times 6 =$ _____

21 $3 \times 9 =$ _____

_____

_____

Find the missing number.

22 $9 \times \boxed{} = 18$

23 $9 \times \boxed{} = 36$

24 $9 \times \boxed{} = 81$

25 $9 \times \boxed{} = 27$

Find each product.

26 $9 \times 2 =$ _____

27 $0 \times 9 =$ _____

28 $9 \times 7 =$ _____

29 $10 \times 9 =$ _____

30 $9 \times 8 =$ _____

31 $6 \times 9 =$ _____

32 $9 \times 11 =$ _____

33 $4 \times 9 =$ _____

Solve.

34 MONEY   Nadina has saved $7 each week for 9 weeks. Paula has saved $9 each week for 8 weeks. Who has saved more? How much more?

_____

35 SOFTBALL   There are 8 teams in the North Town softball league. There are 9 players on each team. How many softball players are in the league?

_____

36 FOOD   A cafeteria prepared 7 pans of baked chicken. Each pan holds 9 pieces of chicken. How many pieces are there in all?

_____

Copyright © by The McGraw-Hill Companies, Inc.

Vocabulary Check   **Write the vocabulary word that completes each sentence.**

37 A number that is multiplied by another number is a(n) _____.

38 **Writing in Math**   Write multiplication sentences for multiplying 9 by the numbers 1 through 10. Explain any pattern that you notice in the products.

_____

_____

_____

 Spiral Review

Solve. (Lesson 3-4, p. 119)

39 **ART CLASS**   Mrs. Rodriguez has 24 students in her art class. Each table seats 8 students. How many tables does Mrs. Rodriguez need for each student to have a seat? Write the multiplication fact that helped you find the answer.

_____

Draw an array to model each multiplication fact. Find the product. Then write the related multiplication facts. (Lesson 3-3, p. 111)

40 $2 \times 7 =$ _____

_____

```
┌────────────────────────┐
│                        │
└────────────────────────┘
```

41 $7 \times 5 =$ _____

_____

```
┌──────────────────┐
│                  │
│                  │
│                  │
└──────────────────┘
```

Copyright © by The McGraw-Hill Companies, Inc.

Draw an array to model each multiplication fact. Find the product. Then write the related multiplication facts.

1 $9 \times 9 =$ ___

_____

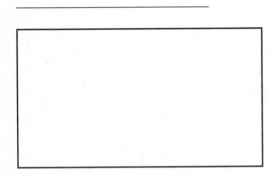

2 $8 \times 4 =$ ___

_____

Find the missing number.

3 $9 \times \boxed{} = 45$

4 $8 \times \boxed{} = 40$

5 $9 \times \boxed{} = 27$

6 $8 \times \boxed{} = 16$

Find each product.

7 $11 \times 8 =$ _____

8 $9 \times 8 =$ _____

9 $6 \times 8 =$ _____

10 $0 \times 9 =$ _____

11 $8 \times 6 =$ _____

12 $6 \times 9 =$ _____

13 $9 \times 4 =$ _____

14 $8 \times 7 =$ _____

Solve.

15 **DRAMA** There are 32 people attending a school play. Arrange the chairs in equal rows. Draw a picture of how the chairs could be arranged in equal rows. Explain the arrangements you drew.

_____

_____

16 **PUZZLES** Suppose the product of the digits of a two-digit number is 8. The sum of the digits is 9. Find the number.

_____

Copyright © by The McGraw-Hill Companies, Inc.

Study Guide

Vocabulary and Concept Check

array, *p. 98*

fact family, *p. 98*

factor, *p. 119*

multiple, *p. 98*

product, *p. 119*

Label each diagram below. Write the correct vocabulary term in each blank.

1 _____

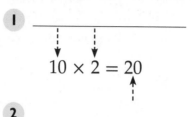

$10 \times 2 = 20$

2 _____

3 _____

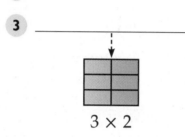

3×2

Lesson Review

3-1 Multiply by 4 (pp. 98–104)

Find each product.

4 $4 \times 4 =$ _____

5 $4 \times 12 =$ _____

6 $1 \times 4 =$ _____

7 $9 \times 4 =$ _____

Use an array to find the missing number.

8 $4 \times \boxed{} = 32$

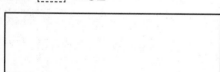

9 $20 = 4 \times \boxed{}$

Example 1

Use an array to find the missing number.

$4 \times \boxed{} = 28$

1. The factor shown is 4. The array will have 4 rows.

2. Make columns until there are 28 rectangles. How many columns do you make? **7**

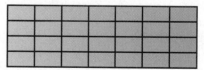

7 columns of 4 rows make 28 rectangles.

3. $4 \times 7 = 28$

Copyright © by The McGraw-Hill Companies, Inc.

3-2 Multiply by 6 (pp. 105–110)

Find each product by using repeated addition.

10 $5 \times 6 =$ _____

_____

11 $6 \times 9 =$ _____

_____

12 $7 \times 6 =$ _____

_____

13 $6 \times 8 =$ _____

_____

Example 2

Find the product of 6 and 4 by using repeated addition. Then write two related multiplication facts.

1. What is the first factor? **6**

2. What is the second factor? **4**

3. Write the product of 6 and 4 as repeated addition.

$$6 + 6 + 6 + 6 = 24$$

4. Write one multiplication fact. $6 \times 4 = 24$

5. Write the related multiplication fact.

$$4 \times 6 = 24$$

3-3 Multiply by 7 (pp. 111–117)

Use an array to find the missing number.

14 $7 \times \boxed{} = 63$

Find each product.

15 $8 \times 7 =$ _____

16 $7 \times 4 =$ _____

17 $1 \times 7 =$ _____

18 $7 \times 7 =$ _____

Example 3

Draw an array to model 7×2. Find the product. Then write the related multiplication facts.

1. The first factor is 7, so there will be 7 rows.

2. The second factor is 2, so there will be 2 columns.

3. Label the array 7×2. Count the number of rectangles. **14**

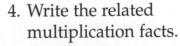

7×2

4. Write the related multiplication facts.

$7 \times 2 = 14$

$2 \times 7 = 14$

Copyright © by The McGraw-Hill Companies, Inc.

3-4 Multiply by 8 (pp. 119–124)

Find the missing number.

19 $8 \times \boxed{} = 40$

20 $7 \times 8 = \boxed{}$

21 $8 \times \boxed{} = 32$

22 $\boxed{} \times 8 = 24$

Find each product.

23 $8 \times 8 =$ _____

24 $6 \times 8 =$ _____

Example 4

Find the missing number.

$8 \times \boxed{} = 56$

1. What number times 8 equals 56?

2. The missing number is **7**.

   $8 \times 7 = 56$

3-5 Multiply by 9 (pp. 125–131)

Find the missing number.

25 $9 \times \boxed{} = 18$

26 $9 \times \boxed{} = 54$

27 $9 \times \boxed{} = 90$

28 $9 \times \boxed{} = 27$

Find each product.

29 $9 \times 8 =$ _____

30 $7 \times 9 =$ _____

Example 5

Find the missing number.

$9 \times \boxed{} = 81$

1. Think about the multiplication facts you have learned. What number times 9 equals 81?

   $9 \times 6 = 54$ $9 \times 7 = 63$

   $9 \times 8 = 72$ $9 \times 9 = 81$

2. $9 \times 9 = 81$

Copyright © by The McGraw-Hill Companies, Inc.

1 Draw an array to model the multiplication fact. Find the product. Then write the related multiplication facts.

$4 \times 3 =$ _____

_____

Find each product by using repeated addition.

2 $6 \times 3 =$ _____

3 $2 \times 7 =$ _____

_____

_____

4 $8 \times 4 =$ _____

5 $9 \times 3 =$ _____

_____

_____

Find each product.

6 $8 \times 6 =$ _____

7 $6 \times 7 =$ _____

8 $6 \times 10 =$ _____

9 $0 \times 9 =$ _____

10 $7 \times 2 =$ _____

11 $7 \times 7 =$ _____

12 $3 \times 8 =$ _____

13 $4 \times 6 =$ _____

14 $8 \times 7 =$ _____

15 $6 \times 6 =$ _____

16 $8 \times 8 =$ _____

17 $9 \times 6 =$ _____

Draw an array to model each multiplication fact. Find the product. Then write the related multiplication facts.

18 $3 \times 8 =$ _____

19 $6 \times 11 =$ _____

_____

_____

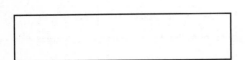

Copyright © by The McGraw-Hill Companies, Inc.

Find each missing number.

20 $6 \times \boxed{} = 54$

21 $5 \times \boxed{} = 40$

22 $4 \times \boxed{} = 28$

23 $9 \times \boxed{} = 27$

24 $7 \times \boxed{} = 21$

25 $8 \times \boxed{} = 64$

Solve.

26 SWIMMING Mr. Castillo teaches 6 swimming classes at the community pool. Each class has 8 students. How many students does Mr. Castillo teach in all?

_____

27 WATER Victoria drinks 8 glasses of water every day. How many glasses of water does she drink in a week?

_____

28 TRANSPORTATION Mr. Pai drives his daughter to school each morning. He picks her up from school each afternoon. Each trip is 9 miles long. How many miles does he drive each day to and from the school?

_____

Correct the mistakes.

29 Megan told Kendrick that any time you multiply by 9, the digits have a sum of 9. Kendrick told her that this was not right. Can you give an example of a time when the sum of the factors is not 9?

_____

_____

_____

Copyright © by The McGraw-Hill Companies, Inc.

STOP

Choose the best answer and fill in the corresponding circle on the sheet at right.

1 Toru eats a salad 8 days a month. His friend Oliver eats a salad twice as often each month. Which math sentence shows how many salads Oliver eats per month?

    A $3 \times 8 = 24$ **C** $8 \times 8 = 64$

    B $8 + 2 = 10$ **D** $8 \times 2 = 16$

2 $\boxed{} \times 4 = 36$

    A 8   **C** 9

    B 7   **D** 6

3 Which expression has the same value as $6 + 6 + 6 + 6 + 6 + 6$?

    A $6 + 6$ **C** $30 - 6$

    B 6×6 **D** $6 - 6$

4 Babette earns $8 an hour. If she works for 6 hours, how much will she have earned?

    A $14   **C** $36

    B $48   **D** $60

5 Find the product of 10 and 7.

    A 3   **C** 17

    B 700   **D** 70

6 Evita is making crafts. She uses 8 feathers for each craft. She makes 9 crafts. How many feathers does she use?

    A 64 feathers

    B 71 feathers

    C 63 feathers

    D 72 feathers

7 Which numbers multiply to give a product of 54?

    A 5×4 **C** 7×8

    B 9×6 **D** 8×6

8 Lamar writes 8 pages of his book each day. How many pages does Lamar write in a week (7 days)?

    A 15   **C** 49

    B 56   **D** 63

9 A bag of apples costs $6. Jonas buys 7 bags. How much does he spend on apples?

    A $13   **C** $42

    B $36   **D** $49

GO ON

Copyright © by The McGraw-Hill Companies, Inc.

10 Jamila bought 7 CDs. How much did she spend?

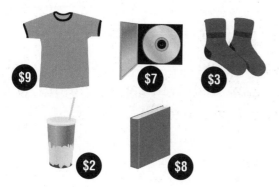

$9 $7 $3 $2 $8

   A $49

   B $48

   C $42

   D $54

11 Which product does *not* equal 36?

   A 6 × 6

   B 1 × 36

   C 7 × 6

   D 9 × 4

12 Yago is placing 48 dishes into boxes. He would like to place 8 dishes in each box. How many boxes will he need?

   A 6

   B 7

   C 42

   D 56

Copyright © by The McGraw-Hill Companies, Inc.

ANSWER SHEET

Directions: Fill in the circle of each correct answer.

1	Ⓐ	Ⓑ	Ⓒ	Ⓓ
2	Ⓐ	Ⓑ	Ⓒ	Ⓓ
3	Ⓐ	Ⓑ	Ⓒ	Ⓓ
4	Ⓐ	Ⓑ	Ⓒ	Ⓓ
5	Ⓐ	Ⓑ	Ⓒ	Ⓓ
6	Ⓐ	Ⓑ	Ⓒ	Ⓓ
7	Ⓐ	Ⓑ	Ⓒ	Ⓓ
8	Ⓐ	Ⓑ	Ⓒ	Ⓓ
9	Ⓐ	Ⓑ	Ⓒ	Ⓓ
10	Ⓐ	Ⓑ	Ⓒ	Ⓓ
11	Ⓐ	Ⓑ	Ⓒ	Ⓓ
12	Ⓐ	Ⓑ	Ⓒ	Ⓓ

Success Strategy

Read each problem carefully and look at each answer choice. Eliminate answers you know are wrong. This narrows your choices even before solving the problem.

STOP

Introduction to Division

How many fish will penguins eat?

Suppose a zoo keeper has 30 little fish for the penguins to eat. If there are 5 penguins, how many fish will each penguin eat? You can use division to answer this question.

STEP **1** Quiz

Are you ready for Chapter 4? Take the Online Readiness Quiz at *macmillanmh.com* to find out.

STEP **2** Preview

Get ready for Chapter 4. Review these skills and compare them with what you will learn in this chapter.

What You Know	What You Will Learn
You know that addition and subtraction are inverse operations. **Example:** $4 + 7 = 11$ $11 - 7 = 4$ **TRY IT!** Rewrite each equation using an inverse operation. **1** $10 + 3 = 13$ _____ **2** $9 + 6 = 15$ _____	*Lesson 4-1* **Multiplication** and **division** are also **inverse operations**. $3 \times 2 = 6$ $6 \div 3 = 2$ $2 \times 4 = 8$ $8 \div 2 = 4$
You know that a fact family has related addition and subtraction sentences. **Example:** $15 + 5 = 20$ $5 + 15 = 20$ $20 - 5 = 15$ $20 - 15 = 5$ **TRY IT!** Write a fact family for 5, 7, and 12. **3** ___ + ___ = ___ ___ + ___ = ___ ___ − ___ = ___ ___ − ___ = ___	*Lesson 4-2 through 4-4* You can use multiplication facts to find **quotients**. $15 \div 5 = \boxed{}$ What multiplication fact has a product of 15 and a factor of 5? $5 \times 3 = 15$ What is the missing factor? 3 Write the division fact. $15 \div 5 = 3$ The quotient is 3.

Relate Multiplication and Division

KEY Concept

Multiplication and **division** are opposite, or **inverse operations**. They undo each other.

There are 3 pairs of shoes. Each pair has 2 shoes. There are 6 shoes in all.

3	×	2	=	6
factor		factor		product

There are 6 shoes in all. There are 2 shoes in each pair. There are 3 pairs of shoes.

6	÷	2	=	3
product		factor		factor

In multiplication, the product is the missing number. In division, one of the factors is the missing number.

Copyright © by The McGraw-Hill Companies, Inc.

VOCABULARY

division
the process of separating into equal groups

fact family
a group of related facts using the same numbers.
Example: $5 \times 3 = 15$;
$3 \times 5 = 15$;
$15 \div 3 = 5$;
$15 \div 5 = 3$

inverse operations
operations that undo each other

multiplication
an operation on two numbers to find their product; it can be thought of as repeated addition.

Example 1

Use the wheels on the cars to write related multiplication and division sentences.

1. There are 6 cars, each with 4 wheels. There are 24 wheels in all. **6 × 4 = 24**

2. There are a total of 24 wheels on 6 cars. Each car has 4 wheels. **24 ÷ 6 = 4**

YOUR TURN!

Use the legs on the chairs to write related multiplication and division sentences.

1. _____ chairs × _____ legs on each chair = _____ legs in all.

   _____ × _____ = _____

2. _____ legs in all ÷ _____ chairs = _____ legs on each chair.

   _____ ÷ _____ = _____

Example 2

Use the array to write a fact family.

1. Count the number of rows. **3**
   Count the number of counters in each row. **5**

2. There are 15 counters in all.

3. Write a multiplication sentence that describes the number of counters. **3 × 5 = 15**

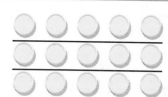

YOUR TURN!

Use the array to write a fact family.

1. How many counters are there in all? _____
   How many counters are there in each row? _____

2. How many rows of counters are there? _____

3. Write a division sentence that describes the number of counters. _____

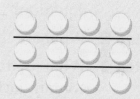

Who is Correct?

Write the fact family for 7, 9, and 63.

Kendall
63 + 7 = 70
63 + 9 = 72
9 × 7 = 63
7 × 9 = 63

Salali
7 × 9 = 63
9 × 7 = 63
63 ÷ 9 = 7
63 ÷ 7 = 9

Manuel
7 + 9 = 16
9 + 7 = 16
16 − 9 = 7
16 − 7 = 9

Circle correct answer(s). Cross out incorrect answer(s). Explain your reasoning.

Copyright © by The McGraw-Hill Companies, Inc.

Use the array to write multiplication or division sentences.

1 ⊙⊙⊙⊙⊙⊙
⊙⊙⊙⊙⊙

There are _____ rows.
There are _____ in each row.
There are _____ counters in all.

Write the multiplication sentence that describes the counters. _____

2 ⊙⊙⊙⊙⊙⊙⊙
⊙⊙⊙⊙⊙⊙⊙

There are _____ counters in all.
There are _____ counters in each row.
There are _____ rows.

Write the division sentence that describes the counters. _____

Step by Step Practice

3 Find the related multiplication facts for $24 \div 3 = 8$.

Step 1 What is the greatest number in this division equation? _____

Step 2 What are the factors? _____ and _____

Step 3 What are the two multiplication equations that contain factors of 3 and 8 with a product of 24?
_____ and _____

Step 4 Draw an array to check.

There are _____ rows of _____ counters.
There are _____ counters in all.

4 Write the related multiplication equations for $10 \div 2 = 5$. _____

_____

5 Write the related multiplication equations for $28 \div 7 = 4$. _____

_____

6 Write the related multiplication equations for $30 \div 10 = 3$. _____

_____

Copyright © by The McGraw-Hill Companies, Inc.

10 Tiles 10 Tiles 10 Tiles 10 Tiles

Problem-Solving Strategies
- ☑ Draw a model.
- ☐ Use logical reasoning.
- ☐ Make a table.
- ☐ Solve a simpler problem.
- ☐ Work backward.

7 HOME IMPROVEMENT   Michele's mom is tiling a kitchen counter. She bought 40 tiles. The counter must be 8 feet wide. How many feet long can the counter be?

Understand   Read the problem. Write what you know.
There are _____ tiles in all.
The counter must be _____ feet wide.

Plan   Pick a strategy. One strategy is to draw a model.

Solve   There are 40 tiles. The counter must be 8 feet wide, so make rows of 8. Count as you make rows until you have used 40 tiles.

The counter will be _____ feet long.

Check   Use multiplication to check your answer.
$5 \times 8 = 40$

8 BALLOONS   Amari invited 6 friends to his birthday party. He wants to give each friend 4 balloons. How many balloons will Amari need? Check off each step.

_____ Understand: I circled key words.

_____ Plan: To solve the problem, I will _____.

_____ Solve: The answer is _____.

_____ Check: I checked my answer by _____.

9 STICKERS   Beth has 30 stickers that she wants to give to 6 friends. Write a division equation to show how many stickers each friend will get if Beth divides the 30 stickers equally. _____

Write a related multiplication equation. _____

GO ON

Copyright © by The McGraw-Hill Companies, Inc.

10 **Reflect** How is writing a multiplication equation the same as writing a related division equation? How is it different?

_____

_____

▶ Skills, Concepts, and Problem Solving

Use the array to write multiplication or division sentences.

11

_____

_____

12

_____

_____

13 Write the fact family for 4, 8, and 32.

_____ _____

_____ _____

14 Write the fact family for 3, 6, and 18.

_____ _____

_____ _____

Solve.

15 **SOCCER** Sam is helping his soccer coach put away soccer balls after a game. Three balls can fit into each bin. Sam fills 6 bins with balls. Write an equation to show how many balls Sam put away. _____

Vocabulary Check **Write the vocabulary word that completes each sentence.**

16 _____ are operations that undo each other.

17 A group of related facts using the same numbers is called a
_____ .

18 **Writing in Math** Why can multiplication be thought of as repeated addition?

_____

_____

STOP

Copyright © by The McGraw-Hill Companies, Inc.

Copyright © by The McGraw-Hill Companies, Inc.

Lesson 4-2 Divide by 2

KEY Concept

Dividing by 2 is one way to split a number in half.

There are several ways to express $16 \div 2$:
- 16 divided by 2;
- the quotient of 16 and 2;
- half of 16.

Use skip counting by multiples of 2 to help you practice and memorize the division facts of 2.

VOCABULARY

dividend
  a number that is being divided

divisor
  the number by which the dividend is being divided

quotient
  the answer or result of a division problem

Example 1

Draw an array to model $14 \div 2$. Then write the division fact.

1. The dividend is 14. There will be a total of 14 rectangles in the array.

2. The divisor is 2. There will be 2 rows.

3. Since half of 14 is 7, there will be 7 columns.

4. Draw the array.

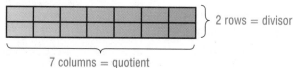

    } 2 rows = divisor

7 columns = quotient

5. Write the division fact.

    14   ÷   2   =   7
   dividend   divisor   quotient

6. Use multiplication to check.

   $7 \times 2 = 14$

YOUR TURN!

Draw an array to model $8 \div 2$. Then write the division fact.

1. There are _____ total rectangles in the array.

2. There are _____ rows in the array.

3. There are _____ rectangles in each row of the array.

4. Draw the array.

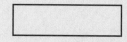

_____ rows = divisor

_____ columns = quotient

5. Write the division fact.

    8   ÷   2   =   _____
  dividend   divisor   quotient

6. Use multiplication to check.

_____

GO ON

Example 2

Use multiplication to find 10 ÷ 2.

1. What multiplication fact has a product of 10 and a factor of 2?

$$\underset{\text{factor}}{5} \quad \times \quad \underset{\text{factor}}{2} \quad = \quad \underset{\text{product}}{10}$$

2. The missing factor is 5.

3. Write the related division fact.

$$\underset{\text{dividend}}{10} \quad \div \quad \underset{\text{divisor}}{2} \quad = \quad \underset{\text{quotient}}{5}$$

4. Draw an array to check.

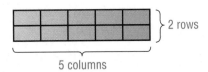

2 rows

5 columns

There are 10 rectangles in all.
There are 2 rows with
5 rectangles in each row.

YOUR TURN!

Use multiplication to find 16 ÷ 2.

1. What multiplication fact has a product of 16 and a factor of 2?

$$\underset{\text{factor}}{\underline{\hspace{1cm}}} \quad \times \quad \underset{\text{factor}}{2} \quad = \quad \underset{\text{product}}{16}$$

2. What is the missing factor? _____

3. Write the related division fact.

$$\underset{\text{dividend}}{16} \quad \div \quad \underset{\text{divisor}}{2} \quad = \quad \underset{\text{quotient}}{\underline{\hspace{1cm}}}$$

4. Draw an array to check.

There are _____ rectangles in all.
There are _____ rows with
_____ rectangles in each row.

Who is Correct?

Find the quotient of 18 and 2.

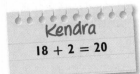

Kendra
18 + 2 = 20

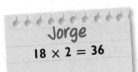

Jorge
18 × 2 = 36

Matt
18 ÷ 2 = 9

Circle correct answer(s). Cross out incorrect answer(s).

Copyright © by The McGraw-Hill Companies, Inc.

▶ Guided Practice

Draw an array to model each quotient. Then write the division fact.

1 Draw an array to show 12 ÷ 2.

Write the division fact.

_____

Use multiplication to check.

_____

2 Draw an array to show 6 ÷ 2.

Write the division fact.

_____

Use multiplication to check.

_____

Step by Step Practice

3 Use multiplication to find 20 ÷ 2.

$$20 \div 2 = \boxed{}$$

Step 1 What multiplication fact has a product of 20 and a factor of 2? _____

Step 2 What is the missing factor? _____

Step 3 Write the division fact. _____

Step 4 Draw an array to check.

_____ rectangles in all.
_____ rows with _____ rectangles in each row.

Use multiplication to find each quotient. Show your work.

4 10 ÷ 2
Write the multiplication fact. _____
What is the missing factor? _____
Write the division fact. _____

5 14 ÷ 2
Write the multiplication fact. _____
What is the missing factor? _____
Write the division fact. _____

6 18 ÷ 2
Write the multiplication fact. _____
Write the division fact. _____

7 22 ÷ 2
Write the multiplication fact. _____
Write the division fact. _____

GO ON

Copyright © by The McGraw-Hill Companies, Inc.

Problem-Solving Strategies
☐ Draw a model.
☐ Use logical reasoning.
☐ Make a table.
☑ Solve a simpler problem.
☐ Work backward.

8 Cecil crept into a cave. He saw 40 bat eyes peering back at him. How many bats did Cecil see?

$$40 \div 2 = \boxed{}$$

Understand	Read the problem. Write what you know. There are _____ eyes for each bat. There are _____ eyes.
Plan	Pick a strategy. One strategy is to solve a simpler problem.
Solve	Think: $4 \div 2 = 2$, so $40 \div 2 = 20$. There are _____ bats.
Check	Use multiplication to check your answer. $20 \times 2 = 40$, so $40 \div 2 = 20$.

9 **SHARING** Rasheed and his brother want to divide 24 grapes between them equally. How many grapes will each brother get? Check off each step.

_____ Understand: I circled key words.

_____ Plan: To solve the problem, I will _____ .

_____ Solve: The answer is _____ .

_____ Check: I checked my answer by _____ .

10 **SHOES** Maria has 8 shoes. There are 2 shoes in each pair. How many pairs of shoes does Maria have?

_____

11 **Reflect** How is dividing by 2 like separating a number into halves?

_____

_____

Copyright © by The McGraw-Hill Companies, Inc.

Skills, Concepts, and Problem Solving

Draw an array to model. Then find each quotient.

12 $12 \div 2 = $ _____

13 $18 \div 2 = $ _____

Find each quotient.

14 $20 \div 2 = $ _____

15 $16 \div 2 = $ _____

16 $22 \div 2 = $ _____

17 $14 \div 2 = $ _____

18 $32 \div 2 = $ _____

19 $42 \div 2 = $ _____

20 $26 \div 2 = $ _____

21 $48 \div 2 = $ _____

22 $34 \div 2 = $ _____

23 $28 \div 2 = $ _____

24 $50 \div 2 = $ _____

25 $60 \div 2 = $ _____

Vocabulary Check **Write the vocabulary word that completes each sentence.**

26 The number that is being divided is called the _____.

27 The _____ is the answer or result of a division problem.

28 **Writing in Math** How can you use multiplication to check the answer to a division problem?

_____

_____

_____

Spiral Review

Solve. (Lesson 4-1, p. 142)

29 Write the related multiplication facts for $20 \div 4 = 5$.

_____

30 Use multiplication to find $30 \div 2$.

_____

STOP

Copyright © by The McGraw-Hill Companies, Inc.

Find the related multiplication equations.

1 $36 \div 4 = 9$

_____

2 $56 \div 8 = 7$

_____

3 $40 \div 10 = 4$

_____

4 $25 \div 5 = 5$

_____

Draw an array to model and find each quotient.

5 $14 \div 2 =$ _____

6 $10 \div 2 =$ _____

Write the multiplication and division fact family.

7 3, 4, and 12

_____

_____

_____

_____

8 5, 7, and 35

_____

_____

_____

_____

Find the quotient.

9 $12 \div 2 =$ _____

10 $18 \div 2 =$ _____

11 $20 \div 2 =$ _____

12 $30 \div 2 =$ _____

Solve.

13 **SAVINGS** Kimi saves half of the money she gets from babysitting to buy a new journal. If Kimi gets $50 from babysitting, how much will she save? _____

14 **DISHES** Stan is loading the dishwasher with drinking glasses. He has 12 glasses to place evenly in 2 rows. Write an equation to show how many drinking glasses go in each row. _____

Copyright © by The McGraw-Hill Companies, Inc.

Divide by 5

KEY Concept

Dividing by 5 means separating into groups of 5.

Use an array to model division. The **quotient** is the total number of rectangles divided by the number of rows.

$$10 \div 5 = 2$$

Since multiplication and division are inverse operations, a missing **factor** in the equation can be used to find the quotient.

$$5 \times \underline{\hspace{2cm}} = 10$$

$$5 \times 2 = 10, \text{ so } 10 \div 5 = 2.$$

VOCABULARY

factor
a number that divides into a whole number evenly; also a number that is multiplied by another number

multiple
a multiple of a number is the product of that number and any whole number

product
the answer or result of a multiplication problem; it also refers to expressing a number as the product of its factors

quotient
the answer or result of a division problem

Use skip counting by **multiples** of 5 to help you practice and memorize division facts with 5.

Example 1

Draw an array to model 45 ÷ 5. Then write the division fact.

1. Count the number of rectangles in the array. **45**

2. How many rows are in the array? **5**

3. Draw the array.

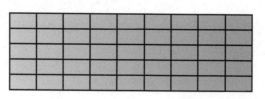

4. How many rectangles are in each row? **9**

5. Write the division fact.
   45 ÷ 5 = 9

6. Use multiplication to check.
   9 × 5 = 45

GO ON

Copyright © by The McGraw-Hill Companies, Inc.

YOUR TURN!

Draw an array to model and find 30 ÷ 5. Then write the division fact.

1. There are _____ total rectangles in the array.

2. How many rows are in the array? _____

3. Draw the array.

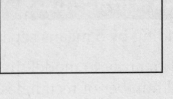

4. How many rectangles are in each row? _____

5. Write the division fact. 30 ÷ 5 = _____

6. Use multiplication to check. _____

Example 2

Find 45 ÷ 5.

1. Write a multiplication equation that will help you find the quotient.

$$5 \times \underline{\hspace{1cm}} = 45$$

2. Skip count by 5s to 45 to find the missing factor. Count the multiples.

$$\begin{array}{ccccccccc} 1 & 2 & 3 & 4 & 5 & 6 & 7 & 8 & 9 \end{array}$$
5, 10, 15, 20, 25, 30, 35, 40, 45

3. The 9th multiple of 5 is 45.

4. So, the missing factor is 9.

$$5 \times 9 = 45$$

5. The missing factor is the quotient of the division equation.

$$45 \div 5 = 9$$

6. Draw a picture to check.

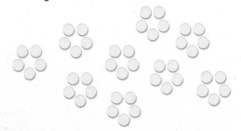

YOUR TURN!

Find 25 ÷ 5.

1. Write a multiplication equation that will help you find the quotient.

_____

2. Skip count by 5s to 25 to find the missing factor. Count the multiples.

$$\begin{array}{ccccc} 1 & 2 & 3 & 4 & 5 \end{array}$$
_____ _____ _____ _____ _____

3. The _____ multiple of 5 is 25.

4. So, the missing factor is _____.

$$5 \times \underline{\hspace{1cm}} = 25$$

5. The quotient of the division equation is

$$25 \div 5 = \underline{\hspace{1cm}}$$

6. Draw a picture to check.

Copyright © by The McGraw-Hill Companies, Inc.

Who is Correct?

Divide 40 by 5.

Ricardo
5 × 8 = 40

Dawn
40 ÷ 8 = 5

Rosana
40 ÷ 5 = 8

Circle correct answer(s). Cross out incorrect answer(s).

 Guided Practice

Draw an array to model the quotient. Then write the division fact.

1 55 ÷ 5

Write the division fact.

_____ ÷ _____ = _____

2 20 ÷ 5

Write the division fact.

_____ ÷ _____ = _____

Step by Step Practice

3 Use a multiplication equation to find 60 ÷ 5.

Step 1 What multiplication equation has 5 as a factor and 60 as a product? _____

Step 2 Skip count by 5s. Which multiple of 5 is 60? _____

Step 3 The missing factor is _____.

Step 4 Write the division fact. 60 ÷ 5 = _____

Step 5 The quotient is _____.

Step 6 Draw an array to check.

_____ rectangles in all.
_____ rows with
_____ rectangles in
each row.

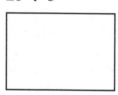

GO ON

Copyright © by The McGraw-Hill Companies, Inc.

4 Use a multiplication equation to find $35 \div 5$.
What multiplication equation has 5 as a factor and 35
as a product? _____

Skip count by 5s. Which multiple of 5 is 35?_____

What is the missing factor? _____

Write the division fact. _____

What is the quotient? _____

Write the division fact. Find the quotient.

5 $25 \div 5$
Write the division fact. _____

The quotient is _____.

6 $40 \div 5$
Write the division fact. _____

The quotient is _____.

Step by Step Problem-Solving Practice

Problem-Solving Strategies
☐ Draw a model.
☐ Use logical reasoning.
☑ Make a table.
☐ Solve a simpler problem.
☐ Work backward.

7 SCIENCE   Mr. Piper places 5 drops of water in
each test tube for a science experiment. If he places
75 drops of water, how many test tubes does he use?

Understand   Read the problem. Write what
you know.

Mr. Piper places _____ drops of water.
There are _____ drops of water in each test tube.

Plan   Pick a strategy. One strategy is to make a table.

Make a table with two rows. Title the first row
"drops of water" and the second row "test tubes."

Solve   There are 75 drops of water in all, arranged in
groups of 5. Skip count by 5s to 75.

drops of water	5	10	15	20	25	30	35	40							
test tubes	1	2	3	4											

Check   Draw a picture to check your work.

Copyright © by The McGraw-Hill Companies, Inc.

8 MARBLES Luisa is sorting marbles into groups. She puts 5 marbles in each group. If Luisa has 60 marbles, how many groups of marbles will she have? Check off each step.

_____ Understand: I circled key words.

_____ Plan: To solve the problem, I will _____.

_____ Solve: The answer is _____.

_____ Check: I checked my answer by _____.

Solve.

9 PUPPIES There are 30 puppies at the pet store. Each showcase can hold 5 puppies. How many showcases does the store need? _____

10 MONEY How many nickels does Sharon need to make 50¢?

_____

11 Reflect How can a multiplication equation help you find the quotient?

_____

_____

_____

![play icon] **Skills, Concepts, and Problem Solving**

Write the division fact. Find the quotient.

12 $40 \div 5$
Write the division fact. _____
What is the quotient? _____

13 $65 \div 5$
Write the division fact. _____
What is the quotient? _____

Find each quotient.

14 $15 \div 5 =$ _____

15 $35 \div 5 =$ _____

16 $80 \div 5 =$ _____

17 $25 \div 5 =$ _____

18 $50 \div 5 =$ _____

19 $95 \div 5 =$ _____

GO ON →

Copyright © by The McGraw-Hill Companies, Inc.

Find each quotient.

20 $10 \div 5 =$ _____

21 $30 \div 5 =$ _____

22 $55 \div 5 =$ _____

23 $70 \div 5 =$ _____

24 $45 \div 5 =$ _____

25 $20 \div 5 =$ _____

26 $85 \div 5 =$ _____

27 $60 \div 5 =$ _____

28 $75 \div 5 =$ _____

Vocabulary Check   **Write the vocabulary word that completes each sentence.**

29 A number that divides into a whole number evenly is called a _____.

30 A _____ is the answer or result of a division problem.

31 **Writing in Math**   Omar's teacher asked him to write the quotient for $45 \div 5$. Omar found the missing factor of 9 for the equation $5 \times \boxed{} = 45$. What number should Omar write? Why?

_____

_____

 **Spiral Review**

Solve. (Lessons 4-1, p. 142 and 4-2, p. 147)

32 Find related multiplication equations for $18 \div 6 = 3$.

_____

33 Find related division equations for $7 \times 6 = 42$.

_____

34 Use multiplication to find $24 \div 2$.
Write the multiplication fact. _____
What is the missing factor? _____
Write the division fact. _____

35 **ORANGES**   Kelsey cut 6 oranges in half. How many pieces does she have? _____

 STOP

Copyright © by The McGraw-Hill Companies, Inc.

Divide by One-Digit Numbers

KEY Concept

Division by a one-digit number has four repeating steps.

   1   Divide.

   2   Multiply.

   3   Subtract.

   4   **Regroup** when necessary. Bring down.

Use the steps to divide 24 by 2.

1 **Divide.**
2 tens divided by 2 is 1 ten.

2 **Multiply.**
1 ten multiplied by 2 is 2 tens.

$$\begin{array}{r} 1 \\ 2\overline{)24} \\ -2\!\downarrow \\ \hline 04 \end{array}$$

3 **Subtract.**
2 tens – 2 tens = 0

4 **There is nothing to regroup. Bring down.**
Bring down (↓) 4 ones.

Repeat the steps.

1 **Divide.**
4 ones divided by 2 is 2 ones.

2 **Multiply.**
2 ones multiplied by 2 is 4 ones.

$$\begin{array}{r} 12 \\ 2\overline{)24} \\ -2 \\ \hline 04 \\ -\ 4 \\ \hline 0 \end{array}$$

3 **Subtract.**
4 ones – 4 ones = 0 ones

4 **Regroup and bring down.**
There is nothing to bring down. There are 0 ones remaining.

The quotient is 12.

VOCABULARY

dividend
the number that is being divided

divisor
the number by which the dividend is being divided

quotient
the answer or result of a division problem

regroup
use place value to exchange equal amounts when renaming a number

remainder
the number that is left after one whole number is divided by another

Copyright © by The McGraw-Hill Companies, Inc.

GO ON

Example 1

Use models to find the quotient of 72 ÷ 3.

1. The dividend is **72.** The divisor is **3.**

2. Use 7 ten blocks and 2 ones blocks to show the dividend.

3. Divide the tens blocks into 3 equal groups. Each group has 2 tens blocks.

4. Regroup the remaining tens blocks as ones. There are now 12 ones blocks.

5. Divide the ones blocks into 3 equal groups. Each group has 4 ones blocks.

6. Add a group of tens blocks and a group of ones blocks.
   2 tens + 4 ones = 24

7. The quotient is 24.

8. Multiply to check.

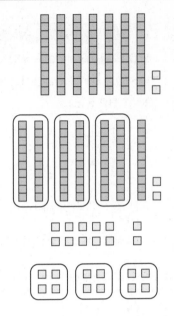

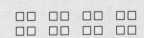

$$\begin{array}{r} 24 \\ \times\ \ 3 \\ \hline 72 \end{array}$$

YOUR TURN!

Use models to find the quotient of 56 ÷ 4.

1. The dividend is _____ . The divisor is _____ .

2. Use _____ tens blocks and _____ ones blocks to show the dividend.

3. Divide the tens blocks into _____ equal groups. Each group has _____ ten block.

4. Regroup the remaining tens blocks as ones. There are now _____ ones blocks.

5. Divide the ones blocks into _____ equal groups. Each group has _____ ones blocks.

6. Add a group of tens blocks and a group of ones blocks.
   _____ ten + _____ ones = _____

7. The quotient is _____.

8. Multiply to check.

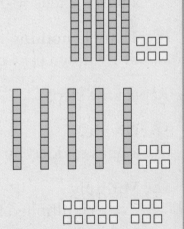

Copyright © by The McGraw-Hill Companies, Inc.

Example 2

Divide 87 by 4.

1. The dividend is 87.
   The divisor is 4.

   $$4\overline{)87}$$
   $$2$$
   $${-8}$$
   $$07$$

2. Divide. $8 \div 4 = 2$

3. Multiply. $2 \times 4 = 8$

4. Subtract. $8 - 8 = 0$

5. Bring down 7 ones.
   There are 7 ones.

6. Divide by 4.
   What number
   multiplied by 4 is no
   more than 7? **1**

   $$21R3$$
   $$4\overline{)87}$$
   $${-8}$$
   $$07$$
   $${-4}$$
   $$3$$

7. Multiply. $1 \times 4 = 4$

8. Subtract. $7 - 4 = 3$

9. The quotient is 21.
   The remainder is 3.

   $$21$$
   $$\times4$$
   $$\overline{84}$$
   $$+3$$
   $$\overline{87}$$

10. Use multiplication to
    check. Add the remainder
    to the product.

YOUR TURN!

Divide 68 by 6.

1. What is the dividend? _____
   What is the divisor? _____

2. Divide. $6 \div 6 =$ _____

3. Multiply. $1 \times 6 =$ _____

4. Subtract. $6 - 6 =$ _____

5. Bring down 8 ones.
   There are _____ ones.

6. Divide 8 by 6.
   What number multiplied by 6
   is no more than 8? _____

7. Multiply. $1 \times 6 =$ _____

8. Subtract. $8 - 6 =$ _____

9. The quotient is _____.
   The remainder is _____.

10. Use multiplication to check.
    Add the remainder to the product.

    _____

Who is Correct?

Divide 53 by 5.

Isabel

$$5\overline{)53}$$
$$1R3$$
$${-5}$$
$$03$$
$${-0}$$
$$3$$

D'Marco

$$5\overline{)53}$$
$$13$$
$${-5}$$
$$03$$
$${-3}$$
$$0$$

Kamilah

$$5\overline{)53}$$
$$10R3$$
$${-5}$$
$$03$$
$${-0}$$
$$3$$

Circle correct answer(s). Cross out incorrect answer(s).

GO ON

Copyright © by The McGraw-Hill Companies, Inc.

Guided Practice

Find each quotient.

1 Divide 48 by 3.

$$3\overline{)48}$$

2 Divide 84 by 4.

$$4\overline{)84}$$

3 Divide 37 by 2.

$$2\overline{)37}$$

 Step by **Step Practice**

4 Find the quotient of $66 \div 5$.

Step 1 Divide 6 tens by 5.
What times 5 is no more than 6? _____

$$5\overline{)66}$$

Step 2 Multiply. Subtract.

Step 3 How many tens remain? _____ Regroup as _____ ones.

Step 4 Bring down 6 ones. 10 ones + 6 ones = 16 ones.

Step 5 Divide 16 ones by 5.
What number multiplied by 5 is no more than 16? _____

Step 6 Multiply. Subtract.

Step 7 How many ones remain? _____

Step 8 What do you multiply to check? _____
Add the _____ to the product.

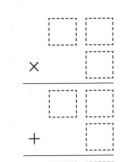

5 $58 \div 3$

6 $69 \div 6$

7 $44 \div 4$

Copyright © by The McGraw-Hill Companies, Inc.

Problem-Solving Strategies

☑ Draw or use a model.
☐ Use logical reasoning.
☐ Make a table.
☐ Solve a simpler problem.
☐ Work backward.

8 SALE   Lorena spent $98 at a sidewalk sale. She bought 2 cell phones. How much did each cell phone cost, if they were the same price?

Understand	Read the problem. Write what you know. Lorena spent _____. She bought _____ cell phones.
Plan	Pick a strategy. One strategy is to draw or use a model.
Solve	Draw or use 9 tens blocks and 8 ones blocks. Divide the tens blocks into 2 equal groups. Each group has _____ blocks. Regroup any remaining tens blocks as ones. There are now _____ ones blocks. Divide the ones blocks into 2 equal groups. Each group has _____ blocks. 40 blocks + 9 blocks
Check	Use multiplication to check your answer. $2 \times 49 = 98$

9 TOKENS   Jaden has 90 bus tokens. If he uses 2 tokens to ride the bus every day, how many days will the tokens last? Check off each step.

_____ Understand: I circled key words.

_____ Plan: To solve the problem, I will _____.

_____ Solve: The answer is _____.

_____ Check: I checked my answer by _____.

Solve. Show your work.

10 SCHOOL   Greenwood School has 88 new desks to share equally between its 6 classrooms. How many new desks will each classroom get? How many desks will be left over?

_____

GO ON

Copyright © by The McGraw-Hill Companies, Inc.

11 Reflect Why is there often a remainder when doing division equations?

_____

_____

▶ Skills, Concepts, and Problem Solving

Solve to find each quotient. Show your work. Write the remainder if there is one.

12 $77 \div 7$

13 $95 \div 4$

14 $66 \div 5$

15 $80 \div 7$

16 $27 \div 2$

17 $39 \div 3$

18 $52 \div 5$

19 $79 \div 2$

20 $65 \div 3$

21 $48 \div 4$

22 $81 \div 3$

23 $97 \div 8$

Copyright © by The McGraw-Hill Companies, Inc.

Solve. Show your work.

24 **WATER** Bottled water costs $8 a case. If Spencer has $80, how many cases of water can he buy?

Spencer can buy _____ cases of water.

25 **BOOKS** Aliya has $75 to buy books. Each book costs $6. How many books can Aliya buy? How much money will she have left over?

Aliya can buy _____ books. She will
have _____ dollars left.

Vocabulary Check   **Write the vocabulary word that completes each sentence.**

26 The number that is left after one whole number is divided by another is called the _____.

27 To _____ means to use place value to exchange equal amounts when renaming a number.

28 **Writing in Math** Explain two different ways that you could find the answer to 90 ÷ 9.

_____

_____

 Spiral Review

Solve. (Lessons 4-2, p. 147 and 4-3, p. 153)

29 Draw a model to find the quotient. Write the quotient. 12 ÷ 2 = _____

```
┌─────────────────────┐
│                     │
│                     │
└─────────────────────┘
```

30 **BEADS** Tito has 65 beads that he wants to make into 5 keychains. Suppose he puts an equal number of beads on each keychain. How many beads will each keychain have? _____

Write the division fact for this problem. _____

STOP

Progress Check 2 (Lessons 4-3 and 4-4)

Draw an array to model and find the quotient. Then write the division fact.

I $35 \div 5$

Write the division fact.

_____ ÷ _____ = _____

2 $40 \div 5$

Write the division fact.

_____ ÷ _____ = _____

Find the quotient. Show your work.

3 Divide 72 by 4.

$4\overline{)72}$

4 Divide 88 by 8.

$8\overline{)88}$

5 $58 \div 3$

$3\overline{)58}$

6 $62 \div 5$

$5\overline{)62}$

Find each missing factor. Write the division fact.

7 $50 \div 5 =$ ___?___

What is the missing factor? _____

Write the division fact. _____

8 $25 \div 5 =$ ___?___

What is the missing factor? _____

Write the division fact. _____

Solve.

9 **LUNCH** Melina's mom bought 20 juice boxes for lunch. If Melina packs her lunch 4 days per week, how many weeks will the juice last? _____

10 **THEATER** Mr. Reilley is taking his 50 students to a musical. There are 8 seats in each row. How many rows will the students need? _____

Copyright © by The McGraw-Hill Companies, Inc.

Vocabulary and Concept Check

dividend, *p. 147*

division, *p. 142*

divisor, *p. 147*

fact family, *p. 142*

factor, *p. 153*

inverse operations, *p. 142*

multiple, *p. 153*

multiplication, *p. 142*

product, *p. 153*

quotient, *p. 147*

regroup, *p. 159*

remainder, *p. 159*

Write the vocabulary word that completes each sentence.

1 _____ are opposite operations that undo each other.

2 The number that is left after one whole number is divided by another is called the _____.

3 A number that is multiplied by another number is a(n) _____.

4 The process of separating numbers into equal groups is called _____.

Label each diagram below. Write the correct vocabulary term in each blank.

5 _____

$$2\overline{)8}^{\,4}$$

6 _____

$$10 \div 5 = 2$$

Lesson Review

4-1 Relate Multiplication and Division (pp. 142–146)

Write the related multiplication equations.

7 15 ÷ 3 = 5 _____

8 28 ÷ 4 = 7 _____

9 36 ÷ 9 = 4 _____

10 50 ÷ 10 = 5 _____

Example 1

Use the array to write a fact family.

1. There are 12 counters.

2. There are 3 rows.

3. There are 4 counters in each row.

4. Write the fact family. 3 × 4 = 12, 4 × 3 = 12, 12 ÷ 3 = 4, 12 ÷ 4 = 3

Copyright © by The McGraw-Hill Companies, Inc.

4-2 Divide by 2 (pp. 147–151)

Find each quotient.

11 $22 \div 2 = $ _____

12 $40 \div 2 = $ _____

13 $12 \div 2 = $ _____

14 $18 \div 2 = $ _____

15 $30 \div 2 = $ _____

16 $14 \div 2 = $ _____

Example 2

Draw an array to model $10 \div 2$. Then write the division fact.

1. The dividend is **10**. There will be a total of 10 rectangles in the array.

2. The divisor is **2**. There will be 2 rows.

3. Since half of 10 is 5, there will be 5 columns.

4. Draw the array.

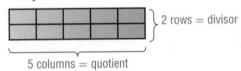

5. Write the division fact.

10	**÷**	**2**	**=**	**5**
dividend		divisor		quotient

6. Use multiplication to check. $5 \times 2 = 10$

4-3 Divide by 5 (pp. 153–158)

Find each missing factor.
Write the division fact.

17 $20 \div 5 = $ _____
What is the missing factor? _____
Write the division fact. _____

18 $45 \div 5 = $ _____
What is the missing factor? _____
Write the division fact. _____

Find the quotient.

19 $40 \div 5 = $ _____   20 $15 \div 5 = $ _____

21 $55 \div 5 = $ _____   22 $30 \div 5 = $ _____

Example 3

Find $35 \div 5$.

1. Write a multiplication equation that will help you find the quotient. $5 \times $ _____ $= 35$

2. Skip count by 5s to 35 to find the missing factor that would make the equation true. Count the multiples.

   1 2 3 4 5 6 7
   5, 10, 15, 20, 25, 30, 35

3. The **7th** multiple of 5 is 35.

4. Complete the multiplication sentence. $5 \times 7 = 35$

5. Use the missing factor to find the quotient. $35 \div 5 = 7$

Copyright © by The McGraw-Hill Companies, Inc.

4-4 Divide by One-digit Numbers (pp. 159–165)

Find the quotient. Show your work.

23 $72 \div 3$

24 $60 \div 4$

25 $96 \div 6$

26 $98 \div 7$

27 $62 \div 5$

28 $35 \div 2$

29 $80 \div 5$

30 $81 \div 3$

31 $79 \div 4$

32 $52 \div 4$

Example 4

Divide 56 by 3.

1. The dividend is 56.

2. The divisor is 3.

3. Divide 5 tens by 3. What times 3 is no more than 5? **1**

4. Multiply. $1 \times 3 = 3$

5. Subtract. $5 - 3 = 2$ Bring down 6 ones. There are **2** tens and **6** ones. Regroup as **26** ones.

6. Divide 26 ones by 3. What times 3 is no more than 26? **8**

7. Multiply. $8 \times 3 = 24$

8. Subtract. $26 - 24 = 2$. There are **2** remaining ones.

$$\begin{array}{r} 18R2 \\ 3\overline{)56} \\ -3 \\ \hline 26 \\ -24 \\ \hline 2 \end{array}$$

9. Use multiplication to check. Add the remainder to the product.

$$\begin{array}{r} 18 \\ \times\ 3 \\ \hline 54 \\ +\ 2 \\ \hline 56 \end{array}$$

Copyright © by The McGraw-Hill Companies, Inc.

Chapter Test

Write the related multiplication equations.

1 $12 \div 4 = 3$

_____

2 $48 \div 6 = 8$

_____

3 $50 \div 5 = 10$

_____

4 $49 \div 7 = 7$

_____

Write the multiplication and division fact family.

5 4, 9, and 36

_____

_____

_____

6 6, 7, and 42

_____

_____

_____

Draw an array to find the quotient.

7 $16 \div 2 =$ _____

8 $30 \div 5 =$ _____

Find the quotient

9 $18 \div 2 =$ _____

10 $14 \div 2 =$ _____

11 $55 \div 5 =$ _____

12 $35 \div 5 =$ _____

13 $8 \div 2 =$ _____

14 $22 \div 2 =$ _____

15 $40 \div 5 =$ _____

16 $20 \div 5 =$ _____

Copyright © by The McGraw-Hill Companies, Inc.

GO ON

Find the quotient. Show your work.

17 Divide 72 by 6.

$$6\overline{)72}$$

18 Divide 98 by 7.

$$7\overline{)98}$$

19 $41 \div 3$

$$3\overline{)41}$$

20 $58 \div 5$

$$5\overline{)58}$$

Solve.

21 **GARDENING**   Alana wants to plant 15 flowers in her mother's garden. She will use 5 rows and will plant an equal number of plants in each row. How many flowers will there be in each row? _____

22 **VOLLEYBALL**   Asad's friends want to play a game of volleyball. Suppose 12 friends are divided into 2 teams. How many friends will be on each team?

_____

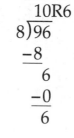

Correct the mistakes.

$$\begin{array}{r} 10R6 \\ 8\overline{)96} \\ -8 \\ \hline 6 \\ -0 \\ \hline 6 \end{array}$$

23 Felicia put an example problem on the board for her class. Some students noticed a mistake. What was her mistake? Show your work.

_____

_____

$$8\overline{)96}$$

STOP

Copyright © by The McGraw-Hill Companies, Inc.

Choose the best answer and fill in the corresponding circle on the sheet at right.

1 What is a related division fact for $3 \times 4 = 12$?

    A $4 \div 3 = 12$ **C** $2 \div 6 = 2$

    B $12 \div 3 = 4$ **D** $12 \div 6 = 2$

2 The answer to a multiplication problem is the _____.

    A quotient   **C** product

    B factor   **D** multiple

3 What equation models the array below?

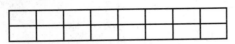

    A $16 \div 4 = 2$ **C** $4 \times 4 = 16$

    B $16 \div 4 = 4$ **D** $16 \div 2 = 8$

4 Halley has 40 shirts to place on 5 shelves. How many shirts can she place on each self?

    A 8

    B 9

    C 10

    D 12

5 What is the missing factor?

$$5 \times \boxed{} = 45$$

    A 9   **C** 10

    B 15   **D** 45

6 Which equation can be used to check $50 \div 10 = 5$?

    A $50 \times 5 = 10$

    B $50 \div 10 = 50$

    C $50 \div 5 = 50$

    D $5 \times 10 = 50$

7 Which division sentence is in the same fact family as $3 \times 6 = 18$?

    A $6 \div 3 = 2$

    B $24 \div 8 = 3$

    C $18 \div 6 = 3$

    D $36 \div 6 = 6$

8 Find the quotient.

$$4\overline{)60}$$

    A 12

    B 15

    C 20

    D 30

GO ON

Copyright © by The McGraw-Hill Companies, Inc.

9 Randall has 10 baseballs. He puts them into 5 cases. Each case has the same number of baseballs. Which picture shows Randall's baseballs?

A

C

B

D

10 Find the quotient.

$$6\overline{)72}$$

A 12R1   C 1R2

B 12   D 10R2

11 Which number makes this equation true?

$$55 \div \boxed{} = 11$$

A 4   C 6

B 5   D 7

12 Elisa wants to place 15 apples into 5 baskets. Each basket will have the same number of apples. How many apples will be in each basket?

A 3   C 5

B 4   D 6

Copyright © by The McGraw-Hill Companies, Inc.

ANSWER SHEET

Directions: Fill in the circle of each correct answer.

1 Ⓐ Ⓑ Ⓒ Ⓓ
2 Ⓐ Ⓑ Ⓒ Ⓓ
3 Ⓐ Ⓑ Ⓒ Ⓓ
4 Ⓐ Ⓑ Ⓒ Ⓓ
5 Ⓐ Ⓑ Ⓒ Ⓓ
6 Ⓐ Ⓑ Ⓒ Ⓓ
7 Ⓐ Ⓑ Ⓒ Ⓓ
8 Ⓐ Ⓑ Ⓒ Ⓓ
9 Ⓐ Ⓑ Ⓒ Ⓓ
10 Ⓐ Ⓑ Ⓒ Ⓓ
11 Ⓐ Ⓑ Ⓒ Ⓓ
12 Ⓐ Ⓑ Ⓒ Ⓓ

Success Strategy

Read the entire question before looking at the answer choices. Watch for words like NOT that change the whole question.

STOP

Copyright © by The McGraw-Hill Companies, Inc.

Copyright © by The McGraw-Hill Companies, Inc.